Physics
Laboratory Experiments

NINTH EDITION

David Pullen
University of Massachusetts – Lowell

Arthur Mittler
University of Massachusetts – Lowell

Walter Schier
University of Massachusetts – Lowell

Mc
Graw
Hill
Education

2 3 4 5 6 7 QVS/QVS 21 20 19 18 17

ISBN-13: 978-1-260-08946-2
ISBN-10: 1-260-08946-0

Solutions Program Manager: Nikki Schmitt
Project Manager: Lynn Nagel
Cover Designer: Fairfax Hutter/Maggie Lytle
Cover Photo Credits: Getty Images

Contents

Section

PART 1

Kinematics & Dynamics

Light

Heat

Electricity & Magnetism

Annex

Introduction I

Objectives of the Laboratory

Physics is an experimental science concerned with the most fundamental aspects of nature, As such it forms the basis of all the physical sciences. Since modern industry and technology are also closely allied with the physical sciences, a thorough familiarity with basic scientific principles is essential to an understanding of our current technology and its evolution.

The most general aims of experimentation in physics, as in any experimental science, are:

i)   to determine through measurement and observation the properties and behavior of the phenomena under study;

ii) to test the validity of any theoretical predictions concerning such properties.

To achieve these aims requires certain fundamental skills and abilities which can only be developed through direct experience in the laboratory. Included among them are an understanding of instrumentation along with basic measurement and analytical techniques, and the abilities to make accurate observations, to evaluate the reliability of experimental data, and to derive conclusions from them. The development of these skills is an important objective of this laboratory program, and the techniques learned will be of value not only in physics but in any scientific or technical area. In addition, this first laboratory course should also serve to clarify and enhance your understanding of the basic principles of physics introduced in your lecture courses, and many of the experiments are designed with this objective in mind.

Pre-Laboratory Preparation

Experiments to be performed will be announced at the start of each semester. It is important that you read all material in the manual referring to the assignment, supplemented by any relevant background material from your textbooks, *before you attend the laboratory*. The laboratory period is not of sufficient length to allow both preparation and experimental work.

Without the equipment in front of you it may be difficult to visualize some aspects of the experimental procedure to be followed. However, you should have a clear understanding of what measurements are to be made at each step of the experiment, and how the experimental data will be analyzed. You may be examined on your preparation by way of a short quiz at the beginning of each laboratory period.

Performing the Experiment

Most of the required equipment will be available on the laboratory bench at the start of each meeting, and any other necessary equipment will be assigned by your Instructor. Do not touch any apparatus until your Instructor has completed the pre-lab. briefing on the experiment.

Follow the procedure outlined in this manual, with any modifications suggested by your Instructor. Always record your measurements as precisely as the equipment will permit. If you are reading a graduated instrument then estimate one significant figure beyond the smallest graduation on the instrument scale. Record the actual reading obtained for a measurement and not just the result obtained after some mental calculation, which may be subject to mistakes. For example, if a micrometer has a zero error of 0.01 mm, then do not correct the actual micrometer readings until after these have been recorded.

For most experiments you will work with a partner. This will enable you to divide the observational work but each should share in all observations and check the other's work for accuracy. You are separately responsible for all measurements taken and although you are encouraged to collaborate and learn from each other, by no means should this lead to two laboratory reports which are essentially identical. Although your reports will be based on the same experimental data, each should reflect a strongly individual effort.

Your recorded experimental data must be reviewed and signed by your Instructor upon completion of the experiment. If no further measurements are suggested, the apparatus may then be disassembled and the equipment replaced as directed by the Instructor.

Safety

Should any apparatus seem to perform improperly, or if there is a question of safety, consult your Instructor immediately. Do not attempt to fix it yourself. Also, in any experiments involving electrical components, your Instructor must first inspect the circuits before you switch on the power source. Scientific equipment is very expensive and often easily susceptible to damage. Always proceed with caution and treat the equipment with due care and respect.

Data Recording

You will need a Data Book in which to record your experimental data, and for this you may use your Laboratory Report Book. Record *in ink* all your original measurements together with any other relevant observations and spot calculations. You will be asked to write a formal report for some experiments and you will need to refer back to this original data. You will find good organization and neatness of your record will pay dividends in avoiding errors and confusion. Your Data Book should provide a permanent record of your original measurements. **NEVER RECORD DATA ON LOOSE PIECES OF PAPER.**

The data for each experiment should be preceded by the name of the experiment, the date, and your partner's name. List also the apparatus used in the experiment together with the identification number of each component. This is valuable if you wish to reassemble the same equipment later to check a measurement, or if there is some doubt concerning the reliability or calibration of a particular instrument. A sketch of the experimental setup, properly labelled, will be necessary if this differs significantly from that in the laboratory manual.

If the experiment involves repeated measurements of the same physical parameters, then these can best be ordered by tabulating the data. The trend of the measurements is more evident when so tabulated, and this affords a better opportunity to spot any errors in the measurements. Each column heading in the table should contain the name or symbol of the measured quantity *and* its units e.g., velocity (m/sec), or T (°C).

Your data record will no doubt contain wrong entries as well as correct ones. However, if you believe an entry to be in error then cancel it with a single, neat line through it - *do not obliterate it*. It is not uncommon that measurements first thought to be wrong turn out later to be correct. Unless the reason is obvious, a word of explanation should be given for any cancelled measurements.

The Laboratory Report

In a professional laboratory the results of an experimental investigation must eventually be communicated as a formal report. This might take the form of an article submitted to a professional journal for publication, or it might be an internal technical report for more limited circulation. Whatever its form, the main purpose is to provide complete information about the experiment and its results. In these introductory courses, its purpose is to provide you with the experience in planning and writing technical reports. These need not be elaborate but should be clear and concise, grammatically correct, and the statements unambiguous. Your report should serve as evidence of independent thinking in which you put into written form the results of a scientific investigation.

In your course, you will be informed of the number and requirements of the technical reports by your instructor and this will depend on the course goals. The following describes the various sections which generally constitute a formal technical report and is intended as a guide to assist you in organizing your report.

Each formal technical report should start with a cover page which has the title of the experiment, your name, the course number, your partner's name, and your instructor's name. The report itself should then comprise the following sections -- *Objective, Introduction, Results and Analysis, Discussion, Conclusions,* and *Answers* (to questions in the manual). The general format is shown below. The Objective and Introduction sections may be kept quite brief. These are covered in detail in the manual which leaves you little room for originality. The remaining sections will count more heavily in grading the report. All tables, diagrams and graphs should be properly numbered (e.g. Table xxx for a table, or Figure x for a diagram or graph) and bear a title or caption to clearly identify what they represent.

Data tables should include the 'raw' measured data from your Data Book, with the experimental uncertainty associated with each measurement written after just the first entry in each column (unless it changes as measurements progress). Experimental results should be presented in graphical form, whenever appropriate, since the analysis of graphs provides an extremely powerful tool in the search for relationships between measured quantities. Allow an entire page for each graph and choose the axis scales so that they conveniently cover the range of the data being plotted. Further details on plotting techniques and graphical analysis are given in Section II. When calculations are largely repetitive a few typical sample calculations will suffice for the report, with the mass of routine calculations confined to the Data Book.

LABORATORY REPORT FORMAT

Objective: This should be a simple statement (one or two sentences) explaining the purpose of the experiment and including any general scientific principle which is under investigation.

Introduction: The underlying theory of the experiment and the experimental procedure should be presented here. Include the derivation of any equations used in the data analysis as well as any useful reference material. Describe briefly how the experiment was performed. This should be written in the past tense (it is an account of what you *did)*, in your own words, and with normal paragraph construction (not as a series of numbered statements as in the manual). Also, avoid using the personal pronoun. If you depart from the procedure described in the manual then this should be explained in more detail. Always include in this section a neat diagram of the assembled apparatus showing the principal parts clearly labeled. Diagrams may be drawn in pencil.

Results and Analysis: In this section your basic experimental data are presented together with any analysis and additional treatment of the data. Whenever possible, summarize your results in tables and in graphical form. These should all be properly numbered and titled. The purely descriptive part of this section may be quite brief and should be concerned primarily with directing the reader to the various tables, calculations and graphs in which the results are presented. Display the answers to your analysis prominently, together with your estimated experimental uncertainties, so that it is clear whether or not you have successfully demonstrated the principle under investigation. Finally, be sure to include the units and dimensions of all physical quantities, whether measured or calculated.

Discussion: Here you should discuss critically the results of your investigation. If the experiment is designed to determine the physical properties of a system or to determine the relationship between certain physical quantities, then what do your results suggest? If the experiment is intended primarily to demonstrate a scientific principle then to what extent does it fulfill this purpose? Always supply whatever proofs are necessary to support your arguments. Your discussion should also include an estimate of the experimental uncertainties in the measurements and their probable sources. What are the principal sources of error in the experiment and what measurements would need to be improved to reduce the uncertainty of the result? If you can think of other ways of improving the experiment then include them here. This is an important section and provides a measure of your understanding of the experiment and ability to think constructively and with originality.

Conclusion: This should be a brief statement (one or two sentences) in which you summarize the results of the experiment. The goals set out in the Objective should be addressed here.

Answers: You may be given specific problems or questions from the manual pertinent to the experiment. These should be answered in discussion style at the end of your report (after the conclusion) and so worded that the question can be ascertained from the answer.

Graphical Methods **II**

Experiments are frequently performed in order to study the manner in which one physical quantity depends upon another. For example, one may wish to determine how the displacement of a moving body varies with time, or how the pressure of a gas depends on its temperature. During the experiment, the *independent* (or *controlled*) *variable*, (e.g. the time and temperature in the above examples) is allowed to change progressively, and corresponding values are measured of the *dependent variable* (e.g., the displacement and pressure in these examples). These data are recorded in tabular form, with corresponding parameters arranged in pairs.

Although such a table contains all available experimental evidence for determining the relationship between the two variables, the relationship can usually be more readily obtained if the experimental data are displayed in the form of a graph, in which values of dependent variable are plotted against corresponding values of the independent variable. Graphical display of the data also serves more effectively to indicate possibly unexpected trends in the relationship, and possible errors in the measurements. Furthermore, once the shape of a graph is well established one can, through interpolation or extrapolation, estimate values of the dependent quantity in regions which were not investigated experimentally. Finally, a graph may be analyzed to determine the mathematical equation which describes the relationship between the plotted quantities.

In the following sections are outlined some basic procedures which should be followed when plotting graphs (part A), and also some techniques in graphical analysis used in determining the mathematical relationships between measured quantities (part B).

A. Preparation of Graphs

Graph paper is available with many different coordinate systems, the most common being rectangular, semi-log, log-log, and polar co-ordinates. The choice of co-ordinate system for plotting experimental data depends on the physical relationship under investigation, but for the majority of studies rectangular co-ordinates are the most convenient and we shall confine this discussion to graphs plotted in the rectangular co-ordinate system.

a) Choice of Axes

In any graph which depicts how two quantities are related to one another, one quantity is usually considered the independent variable, since the values it takes are determined by the experimenter, and the other quantity is the dependent variable. As the independent variable is progressively changed the value of the dependent variable is determined from the experiment at each value of the independent variable.   In almost all cases the independent variable should be plotted along the horizontal or x-axis, sometimes referred to as the *abscissa scale*, with the dependent variable plotted along the vertical or y-axis, also referred to as the *ordinate scale*.

b)   Choice of Scales

The proper choice of scales for the axes is very important.   Graphs should generally be plotted on a full page and the scales for abscissae and ordinates so chosen that the ranges covered by the two variables extend over a large part of the page.   The plotted data points should not be confined to just a small area of the graph paper.   To achieve this it may be necessary in some cases to suppress the origin of one or both axes, i.e., the intersection of both axes need not always correspond to zero values of the two plotted variables.

At the same time, each main division of the graph should be conveniently chosen so that values of the plotted variables can be easily read from the graph.   Divisions corresponding to 1, 2, 4, 5 or 10 units are best; never use values of 3, 6, 7 or 9.

If the variables involve exceptionally large or exceptionally small numbers, this can result in rather cumbersome values for the scale divisions.   To avoid this, use a multiplying factor of a convenient power of 10. For example, if a measured force varies from 10,000 dynes to 80,000 dynes, then a multiplying factor of 10^4 may be used and the scale divisions numbered in the range 1.0 to 8.0, with the factor $\times 10^4$ placed to the right of the largest value on the scale.

c)   Labelling of the Coordinate Scales

In the area outside the scales, label each axis with the name of the quantity being plotted *and* its units.   Standard abbreviations may be used for the units.   Numerical values of the quantities should be indicated on each axis.   These numbers should be regularly spaced and not too crowded. Numbering at every 2, 4 or 5 main scale divisions is usually best.

d)   Data Plotting

Each experimental data point should be recorded on the graph as a fine dot, made with a sharp pencil.   The points should then be enclosed by neat, open circles (called point protectors) to make their locations conspicuous.   Occasionally, more than one set of data may be plotted on the same graph, in which case they should be clearly differentiated from one another by using other symbols, such as squares or triangles, to surround the data points.   If the experimental uncertainty in the dependent variable has also been estimated then this may be indicated for each data point by a vertical bar representing the upper and lower limits of the measurement.

e)   Curve Fitting

A *smooth* curve should be drawn through the average of the data points to show the general trend of the data. **DO NOT** connect successive data points by straight lines. When examining a physical law or functional relationship one usually expects a smooth curve (the term "curve" includes the straight line) to describe the data.

Uncertainties in experimental measurements usually lead to some fluctuation of the data points around the smooth curve and this is referred to as *scatter*. It is unusual for every data point to be on the curve, and the curve should be drawn among the points in such a manner as to minimize the deviation of all data points from it. There should be approximately the same number of data points above and below the 'best-fit' curve. If one or more points lie well away from the curve then the experimental data should be checked to see if an error has been made. If there is no clear explanation for such departure, then the point may, in general, be disregarded, unless repeat measurements confirm its validity.

If more than one set of experimental data are include in the same graph, then a best-fit smooth curve should be drawn through each set. The different data sets can be distinguished from each other by using different symbols for the data points e.g. circles, squares or triangles, or by different line constructions e.g. solid, dotted or dashed lines. In such cases a key should be included in a clear space on the graph to explain the different curves.

Curves should be drawn with mechanical aids, such as French curves or rulers. Always use a sharp pencil and draw up to, but not through, the data circles. The curves should never be allowed to obscure the data points. Any abrupt kinks in a curve should be smoothed out.

f)   Title

Graphs should have a figure number and a short title which accurately describes the purpose of the graph. This should be included near the top of the graph in an open space where it does not interfere with the plotted data.

g)   Slope Measurements

It is often required to measure the slope of a curve since this property frequently has important physical significance. For a straight-line graph the slope is constant, whereas one which has curvature the slope changes from point to point. In this case the slope at a given point is defined as the slope of the tangent to the curve at that point. In measuring a slope one must distinguish carefully between the *geometric slope* and the *physical slope*. The geometric slope is defined to be $\tan \theta$, where θ is the angle between the line (or tangent) and the abscissa axis. This therefore depends on the inclination of the line and hence on the choice of scales for plotting the data. It has little physical significance and no units. In graphical analysis one is always concerned with the physical slope rather than the geometric slope. Suppose, for example, a quantity y is plotted along the ordinate axis and a quantity x is plotted along the abscissa axis. The physical slope at any given point along the resulting curve can be found by drawing a large right-angled triangle, the hypotenuse of which is the tangent to the curve at the given point, and calculating the ratio $\Delta y/\Delta x$ (see Fig. 1 below) using for Δy and Δx the scales and units that have been chosen for the two axes. The physical slope generally has dimensions (its units are simply a ratio of the units chosen for the y- and x-axes) and is independent of the geometrical inclination (θ) of the tangent.

When measuring the physical slope of a straight-line graph, use as much of the line as possible to get the maximum lengths for the sides Δy and Δx. If the line is curved and the physical slope of the tangent to the curve at a given point is required, then make the tangent line conveniently large. This minimizes errors in computing physical slopes due to plotting techniques.

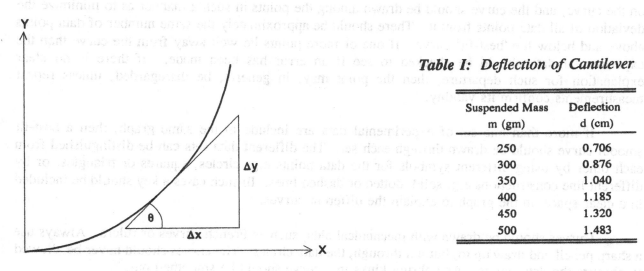

Table I: *Deflection of Cantilever*

Suspended Mass m (gm)	Deflection d (cm)
250	0.706
300	0.876
350	1.040
400	1.185
450	1.320
500	1.483

Figure 1:   *The physical ($\Delta y/\Delta x$) and geometrical (θ) slopes of a curve.*

Example 1

To illustrate some of the features of a graph discussed on the previous pages, we may use the data of Table I which relate the deflection (d) of a cantilever when different loads of mass (m) are hung from its end.

These data are plotted in rectangular co-ordinates in Fig. 2. The deflection, d, (the dependent variable) is plotted on the ordinate scale and the mass, m, (the independent variable) is plotted along the abscissa scale. The plotted quantities are clearly indicated, with their units, on each axis. In labelling the axes, only a few principal values are given. Note also that the origins of the two axes do not appear on the graph. Because of the range of values covered by d and m (approximately 0.7 to 1.5 cm, and 250 to 500 gm, respectively), the origins have been suppressed, since otherwise the plotted data points would be contained only in a small corner of the graph which would make analysis of the graph less accurate.

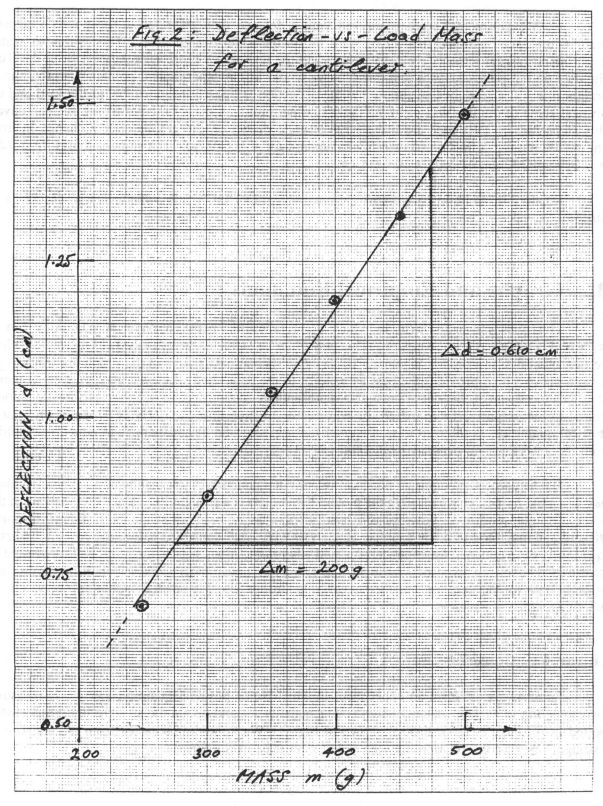

Figure 2. *Deflection of a Cantilever*

Each experimental point is marked with a dot and then encircled. The points suggest a straight line graph although not all of them lie on the same straight line. This is due to scatter (experimental measurements are never exact) and the line drawn represents the best fit to the data. The data do not indicate that a non-linear curve would fit the experimental points any better than a straight line. The straight line shows that the deflection is linearly proportional to the load and the physical slope of the line will yield the deflection per unit load mass (in cm/gm) for this cantilever. This slope can be calculated from the large triangle drawn on the graph. For a change in mass $\Delta m = 200$ gm the deflection changes by an amount $\Delta d = 0.610$ cm. The slope is therefore $\Delta d / \Delta m = 0.610$ cm/200 gm or 3.05×10^{-3} cm/gm.

Finally, in addition to a figure number the graph has a title which clearly describes its purpose.

B.   Graphs and Empirical Equations

The most powerful form in which the relationship between physical quantities can be expressed is a mathematical equation. This may often be extracted from analysis of a graph in which the two quantities are plotted together. If the experimental data points in the graph are joined by a smooth curve which provides the best average fit to the data, then whatever mathematical equation describes the shape of that curve must also represent the relationship between the physical quantities plotted in the graph. This approach, based directly on experiment in deriving an equation relating physical quantities, is referred to as the *empirical method*, and the mathematical equation resulting from the analysis is an *empirical equation*.

Determining the empirical equation relating the quantities under study is a relatively simple task when the best-fit curve through the plotted data points is a straight line, since the analysis of this is very straightforward. If, however, the best fit curve has some other shape the task becomes more difficult and may require many attempts at analysis with 'trial' equations before the correct empirical equation is determined. An experimenter will, therefore, often search for a method of presenting measured data in the form of a straight-line graph (or linear plot) since an analysis of this will quickly lead to the required mathematical relationship (i.e., empirical equation) between the quantities which are plotted.

Linear Relationships

Suppose we perform an experiment in which some physical quantity, say y , is measured corresponding to various values of some other quantity x , and obtain the straight line graph (when plotted in rectangular co-ordinates) shown in Fig. 3. We know immediately from the equation of a straight line that the relation between y and x must be of the form:

$$y \ = \ y_o + ax \qquad\qquad 1)$$

In this equation the slope "a" is given by:

$$a = \frac{\Delta y}{\Delta x} = \frac{y_2 - y_1}{x_2 - x_1} = constant,$$

and the intercept y_o equals the value of y when x = 0.

The constants "a" and "y_o" may be obtained directly from the graph and the experiment thus yields a complete determination of the mathematical relationship (eqn. 1) between the physical quantities x and y.

For a specific example suppose we measure the velocity (v) of a freely falling body after different time intervals (t). If we plot the measured velocity -vs.- time we obtain a graph such as that shown in Fig. 4.

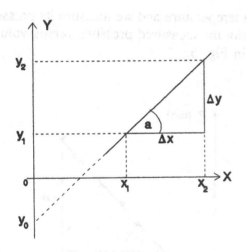

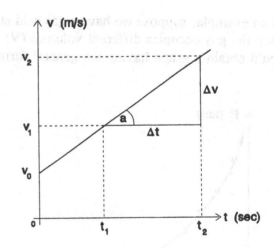

Figure 3: *Plot of y-versus-x in rectangular coordinates.*

Figure 4: *Variation of velocity with time during free-fall.*

It is seen that the velocity increases linearly with time, producing a straight-line graph. The empirical equation relating these quantities will be similar to eqn. 1), except that we now identify y with the velocity v, and x with the time interval t, i.e.,

$$v = v_o + at \qquad \qquad 2)$$

$$\text{where} \quad a = \frac{\Delta v}{\Delta t} = \frac{v_2 - v_1}{t_2 - t_1}$$

and v_o is the initial velocity of the body at t = 0 seconds.

The slope "a" can be identified in this case as the magnitude of the acceleration of the body during free fall (i.e., the acceleration due to gravity = 9.8 meters/sec^2) and the intercept value of the straight line on the velocity axis (t = 0), v_o, is the initial velocity of the body at the instant it went into free fall.

Non-Linear Relationships

Note that in plotting the v-t graph of Fig. 4 we immediately obtain a straight line graph (or linear plot) without the need for further treatment of the experimental data. Extraction of the empirical equation (eqn. 2) is therefore very straightforward in this case. The data for many relationships in science, however, when plotted in rectangular co-ordinates, do not produce a straight line curve of the type $y = y_o + ax$. These are the so-called *non-linear relationships* and an attempt must be made to find a method of plotting which will yield a straight line.

As an example, suppose we have a gas held at constant temperature and we measure its pressure (P) when the gas occupies different volumes (V). If we plot the measured pressure-versus-volume we would obtain a graph having the general form shown in Fig. 5.

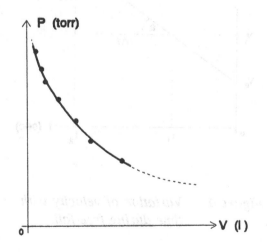

Figure 5: *Variation of pressure P with volume V for a gas at constant temperature.*

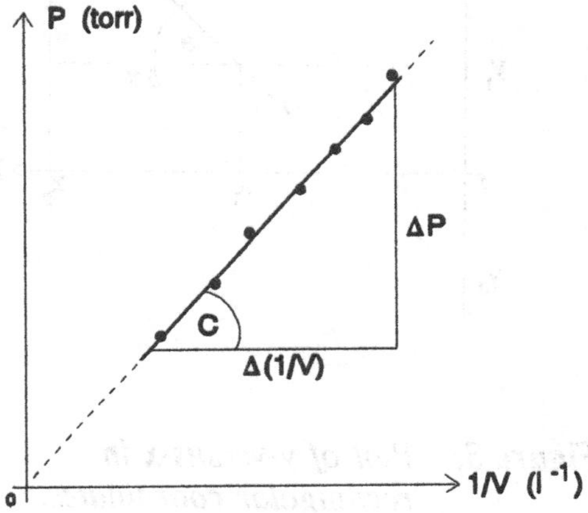

Figure 6: *Variation of P with 1/V for gas at constant temperature. (Same experimental data as for Fig. 5.)*

The curve in Fig. 5 clearly demonstrates that a non-linear relationship exists between P and V, and we are now faced with the task of determining what equation will describe this curve. An experienced observer might suspect the curve to have the shape of a rectangular hyperbola in which case the equation

$$PV = C \quad (C \text{ is a constant})$$

3)

should hold true. In this case -

$$P = C\frac{1}{V}$$

and it is the plot of P -vs.- 1/V which should yield a straight line if the hyperbola guess is correct. Comparison with the general equation for a straight line ($y = y_0 + ax$) suggests the identification of P with y and 1/V with x, the straight line apparently passing through the origin since $y_0 = 0$. Such a plot of P -vs.- 1/V is shown in Fig. 6 where a linear relationship between these two quantities is indeed observed experimentally. The constant "C" in the equation PV = C (which is the well-known Boyle's Law for a gas) can now be determined by measuring the slope of the straight line of Fig. 6.

Note that in attempting to derive the relationship between P and V we held the other possible variable in the experiment, namely the temperature of the gas, at a constant value. If we allow both the temperature and volume of the gas to vary together during the experiment this would compound the problem of determining the relationship between pressure and either one of them. Quite generally, in the empirical method only two physical quantities should be allowed to vary together, with all others being held fixed. For example, if we now wish to examine the dependence of the gas pressure on temperature, then this experiment should be performed with the volume held fixed.

We can see how, with experience and considerable insight, the original experimental data (P and V in the example above) may be suitably arranged to obtain a straight line graph (P-versus-1/V), which then lends itself readily to analysis. Suppose, however, that we are not so blessed with intuition. Fortunately, there is an alternative and powerful analytical technique which often does lead to success in determining the empirical equation, and which we shall discuss next.

Power Law Relationship

Suppose we have measured two physical quantities, u and v say, which when plotted together on rectangular co-ordinate paper produces a curve (Figure 5 is one such example if we identify u with P and v with V). The curve will certainly prove that a non-linear relationship exists between u and v, but of what kind?

Experience indicates that the relationship between two physical quantities is in fact more likely to be in the form of a *power law* rather than a linear relationship, in which case it is prudent for the experimenter to consider next a relationship of the form:

$$u = Av^n \tag{4}$$

where A and the power (or exponent) n are constants to be determined from the experiment. (Note that the linear relationship is merely a special form of the power law in which n = 1). In this case, a plot of u-versus-v^n would produce a straight line with slope A, but we have first to determine the value of n. This can be achieved as follows. By taking logarithms both sides of eqn. 4), this can be re-expressed in the form:

$$\log u = \log (Av^n)$$

or $$\log u = \log A + n \log v$$ 5)

which is now linear in the quantities **log u** and **log v**.

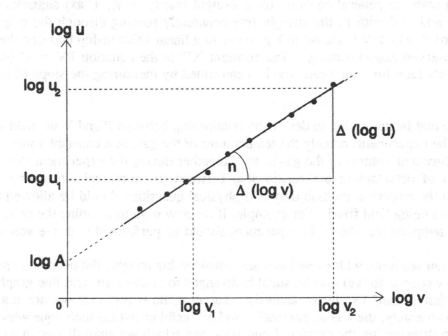

Figure 7: *Log u-versus-log v for the equation u = Av^n.*

Equation 5) has the general linear form $y = y_o + ax$ if we identify log u with y and log v with x. Thus, a plot of log u -*vs.*- log v will produce a straight line graph (Fig. 7) which can be analyzed to determine the constants A and n of the equation. The constant n is now given by the slope of eqn. 5), i.e.:

$$n = \frac{\Delta (\log u)}{\Delta (\log v)} = \frac{\log u_2 - \log u_1}{\log v_2 - \log v_1}$$

The intercept value of log u when log v = 0 provides us with the value for log A. Thus the antilogarithm of this intercept value determines the value of A in eqn. 4).

It should be noted that the exponent n must be a dimensionless quantity. It is in many ways the more interesting constant of eqn. 4) than A, since it expresses a universally fundamental relationship between u and v independent of the individual characteristics of the particular experiment designed to measure u and v. Most often n is a simple integer quantity or the ratio of two small integers. The constant A, on the other hand, is merely a proportionality constant in eqn. 4) which will generally have dimensions, and its value will depend on the units employed to measure u and v and possibly on other parameters in the experiment.

Example 2

A body, initially at rest, is allowed to fall freely under gravity and the distance through which it falls (s) is measured after different time intervals (t). A plot of the measured s -vs.- t shows a non-linear relationship between them, as indicated in Fig. 8.

If we guess at a power law relationship of the form $s = At^n$ and plot log s -vs.- log t, the result will be a straight-line graph (Fig. 9) whose slope is 2. The antilog of the intercept value (log A) will be 4.9 if s is measured in meters and t in seconds. We therefore arrive at the following empirical equation between s and t:

$$s = 4.9 \, t^2$$

A theoretical analysis of this motion yields the equation:

$$s = 1/2 \, g \, t^2$$

where g is the acceleration due to gravity (9.8 meters/sec^2).

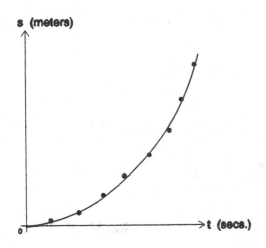

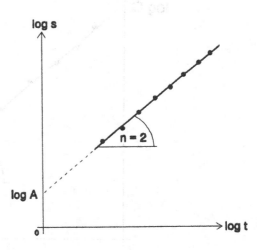

Figure 8:   *Displacement (s) -vs.- time (t) for a body in free fall.*

Figure 9:   *Log s -vs.- log t for a body in free fall. (Same experimental data as for Fig. 8.)*

Example 3

In a previous example we showed that the pressure-volume relationship for a gas was non-linear (Figure 5). Suppose we try a relationship of the form:

$$P = CV^n$$

A plot of log P-versus-log V will yield a straight line graph as shown in Figure 10. Analysis of this graph will yield a slope of -1, thus leading to the empirical equation between P and V of:

$$P = CV^{-1} = C/V$$

or $$PV = C$$

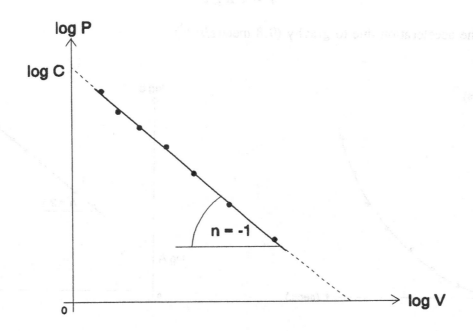

Figure 10: Log P-versus-log V for a gas at constant temperature. (Same experimental data as for Figure 5.)

Summary

The value of casting experimental data into a form which yields a straight line plot should now be evident from the previous discussion. Broadly speaking, such a plot can be easily analyzed to produce the constant required for the empirical equation which describes the relationship between the measured quantities.

We have established the following approach in seeking such a relationship between any two physical quantities y and x:

1. **Linear Relationships:** If a plot of y -vs.- x yields a straight line, then the empirical relationship between them must be linear, having the form $y = y_o + ax$. The constants y_o and a may be determined directly from the intercept and slope of the line.

2. **Non-Linear Relationships - Power Law:** If a plot of y -vs.- x does not yield a straight line, then we may try a power law relationship of the type $y = Ax^n$. If a plot of log y -vs.- log x then yields a straight line its analysis will lead to the values of the constants n and A in the empirical equation. A plot of y -vs.- x^n using the now known value of n will also yield a straight line with slope A.

Application of the power law recipe does not of course guarantee success. Not all physical relationships are of the power law type and are not therefore amenable to that type of analysis. As an example, the angular displacement (θ) of a torsional pendulum as a function of time (t) is described by the equation $\theta = \theta_o \sin(\omega t + \alpha)$ which is not a power law relationship. In such cases the experimenter must be correspondingly more ingenious in attempting to deduce the true empirical equation.

Experiments III

Part 1

Period of Oscillating Ring 1

In this experiment the functional relationship between the period of vibration of a ring and its diameter will be determined.

Introduction

If a ring which is initially hanging at rest from a knife edge is displaced from its equilibrium position and then released, it will oscillate about its equilibrium position (fig. 1). These oscillations will have a characteristic time interval called the period (T), which is the time taken for one complete cycle of oscillation of the ring. The period can be determined by measuring the time it takes for the ring to pass through its equilibrium (or some other) position in its swing to when it next passes through that position moving in the same direction as before.

In this experiment the periods of vibration of several rings having different diameters will be measured. It will be observed that the periods are different for rings with different diameters, showing the period and diameter to be related parameters. The objective of this experiment is to determine from these measurements the functional relationship between the period of a ring and its diameter.

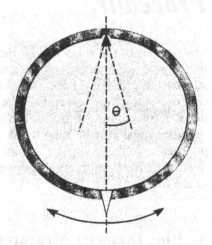

Experience shows that the functional dependence between two related parameters frequently has the form of a **power law**. If this turns out to be true for the vibrating ring, then the period will be proportional to some power (p) of the diameter (D) and we can write:

Figure 1: Oscillating Ring

$$T \propto D^p \quad \text{or} \quad T = kD^p \quad \text{...} 1)$$

where k is a constant of proportionality. Assuming the power law does indeed hold true, our task is now to determine the numerical values of the constants k and p in eqn. 1).

Since T is directly proportional to D^p, a graph of T -vs-D will **not** yield a straight line (unless, by chance, $p = 1$). However, if a smooth curve were to be drawn through the data points, then the slope of this curve would decrease as D increases if $p<1$, whereas the slope would increase with increasing D if $p>1$. Therefore, by observing how the slope of the T -vs-D curve changes as D increases, we can determine whether $p<1$ or $p>1$.

A plot of T -vs- D^p will yield a straight line with a slope equal to k. However, we cannot plot such a graph without first knowing the value of p. We can, of course, use a *trial and error* approach in which different values of p are tried until a straight line is obtained. This may eventually work but is not a very efficient technique.

The constant p can be determined directly if we work instead with the logarithmic form of eqn.1. Taking logarithms on both sides of the equation, we have:

$$\log T = \log(kD^p) = \log k + p \log D \dotfill 2)$$

Since p and $\log k$ are constant quantities, eqn.2 shows that a graph of $\log T$ -vs- $\log D$ will be a straight line with a slope equal to p and an intercept on the $\log T$ axis equal to $\log k$. Both p and k can, therefore, be obtained from the $\log T$ -vs- $\log D$ plot and eqn.1 is completely defined. (If this plot does not, in fact, turn out to be a straight line, then we have to conclude that the power law expressed by eqn.1 does not correctly describe the functional relationship between T and D, in which case we must use some other method to determine the true relationship.)

Procedure

The periods of the rings will be measured using a **photogate**, which comprises both a source and detector of infrared (IR) radiation. A small pointer is attached to each ring immediately below the point of suspension (see fig. 1) and this periodically interrupts the infrared beam to the photogate detector as the ring oscillates back and forth. The detector provides a voltage output whose value depends on whether or not it is receiving infrared radiation from the source. By interfacing the photogate to a computer this voltage signal can be monitored by the computer. The computer senses the resulting changes in the photogate voltage output (5 volts when the IR beam is unblocked and 0 volts when blocked) and, by measuring the time intervals between alternate interrupts, determines the period of successive oscillations of the ring.

A. Ring Diameter Measurements

i)   Using a vernier caliper for the small rings and a meter rule for the large rings, determine the **mean diameter** D (average of the inner and outer diameters) for each ring. Make at least two measurements of the inner (d_i) and outer (d_o) diameters for each ring at different positions around the ring to check that the rings are truly circular, and tabulate your values as shown in Table I.

B. Ring Period Measurements

ii)   The photogate is connected to the computer via an **interface module** having several connecting ports. Plug the photogate into Digital Channel Port #1 on the module. The remaining ports will not be used in this experiment.

iii)   Suspend the largest ring from the knife edge and attach a thin V-shaped pointer at the lowest point on the ring (see fig 1). Masking tape makes a convenient pointer. Position the photogate so that its infrared beam is blocked by the pointer.

iv)   From the computer desktop screen, select (double click on) the program "*VIBRATING RING*". This program opens with a home page (fig. 2). Press the <CTRL R> keys and then enter the last names of all experimenters in your group. Tabs for other pages are shown at the top of this page corresponding to Photogate Test, Data Acquisition, Data Analysis, and Data Summary.

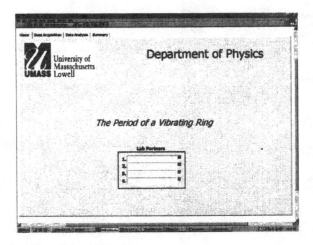

Figure 2: Vibrating Ring home page.

v)   To test that the photogate is operating properly, select **Photogate Test** (see fig. 3) and set the ring oscillating with small amplitude. Follow the test procedure described on this screen.

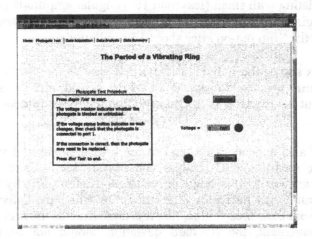

Figure 3: Photogate Test screen.

vi)   Next, select the **Data Acquisition** page (fig. 4). Your remaining ring data for the experiment will be accumulated on this page. In the **Controls** box enter the diameter (in meters) of the mounted ring.

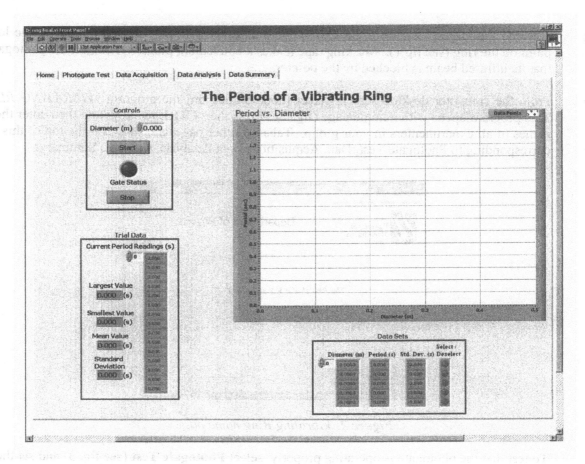

Figure 4: Data Acquisition screen.

vii) Start the ring oscillating with small (less than 10°) **angular amplitude** (angle θ in fig. 1). Press the **Start** button to begin collecting data. The computer will now measure the periods of successive oscillations. Press the **Stop** button after about 15 oscillations.

viii) The **Data Sets** box shows the individual measured periods together with the **mean value** of the period, the **minimum** and **maximum** values of the period, and the **standard deviation** of the measurements about the mean value. (Only the first ten measurements are displayed alongside a scroll button.)

ix) A pop-up window also appears at the end of the measurement and you are asked whether you wish to accept the measurement. Unless you already know there to be a problem with the measurement, the answer to this question is largely determined by the value of the standard deviation. This quantity is a measure of the amount by which the individual period measurements differ on average from their mean value, i.e., it is a measure of the *precision* of the measurements. In a careful measurement, the standard deviation should not be more than about 1ms (1 millisecond = 1×10^{-3} second) for the smallest ring. If this condition is satisfied then the measurement can be accepted and a data point is plotted in the graph of Period –vs.- Diameter and the measurement entered into the table **Data Sets** displayed below the graph. If this condition is not satisfied, then that measurement can probably be improved and it should not be accepted but instead repeated. When not accepted it will not be entered into the table.

x)   Repeat steps vi) to ix) to measure the period of a different ring and continue in this manner until all five rings have been measured. Each time a ring measurement is accepted, the graph and Data Sets table are updated until all five ring measurements are displayed.

xi)   When all measurements are finished, select the five measurements chosen for plotting.

C. Analysis

> *NOTE: If at any time during analysis an accepted ring measurement is believed to be in error, it can be removed from the accepted data set by returning to the Data Acquisition page and pressing its active button to make it inactive. The measurement for that ring must then be repeated to provide a new active measurement and the **Apply Selected Data Set** button pressed again to apply this new set of data to the analysis. The inactive data will be kept in memory and its rejection **must** be explained in your report.*

xii)   Select **Data Analysis**. Several different graphs of the data can be plotted from this page and a secondary menu is shown from which to select either **Linear Plot**, **Power Plot**, or **Log Plot**.

xiii)   Select Linear Plot first (fig. 5) to view a graph of T -vs- D. It should be evident from this that the experimental data cannot be fitted with a straight line so we can conclude that $p \neq 1$ in eqn. 1. Obtain a printout of this page for each partner.

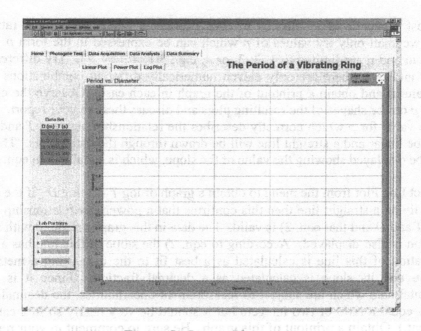

Figure 5: *Linear Plot screen.*

xiv)   Now select "Power Plot" from the menu (fig. 6) to try different values for the exponent p in graphs of T-vs-D^p.

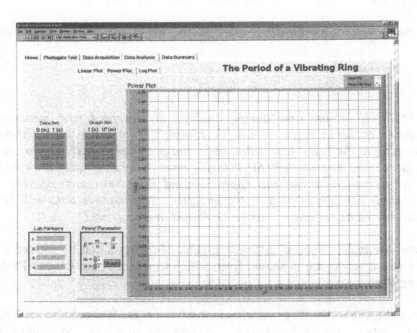

Figure 6*: Power Plot screen.*

xv)   Since most power laws in physics involve exponents which are simple ratios of two small integers, we shall only try values of p which can be expressed in the form $p = m/n$, where the values of m and n are limited to 1, 2, 3, or 4, e.g., 3/1, 4/3 or 2/3. Try different values of p for both $p>1$ and $p<1$ (there are only eleven numerically different combinations for this range of integer values) and obtain a printout of the graph in each case. Observe the effects of different values of p on the shapes of the resulting plots and discuss these in your report. When you finally select the value for p which correctly describes the relationship between T and D, the T-vs-D^p plot will be linear and a straight line will be drawn through the data points. The equation of this line will be displayed showing the value of the slope, which is equal to k in eqn. 2).

xvi)   Next select Log Plot from the menu to obtain a graph of log T-vs- log D. If the data points in this graph all lie on a straight line then this confirms that a power law relationship does indeed exist between T and D and that eqn. 2) is valid. The data in this graph are fitted with a straight line and its equation is also displayed. According to eqn. 2) the slope of this line has a value equal to p. (The equation of this line is calculated as a best fit to the data using a method called **linear regression** and its slope is calculated as a decimal fraction. Since it is determined from experimental data which are subject to measurement uncertainties, the decimal value is unlikely to exactly equal a ratio of two integers but it should be very nearly so in a carefully performed experiment.) Obtain a printout of this graph. Be sure to comment in your report on how well this value of p compares with the value which resulted in a linear plot of T-vs-D^p in the previous step.

xvii)   Finally, select **Data Summary** (fig. 7) and print your table of selected data as well as any deselected data. If you have deselected any data, it is important to explain in your report why these data were rejected.

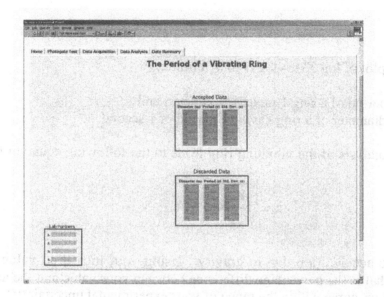

Figure 7: *Data Summary screen*

Further Analysis

i)   From your measured values for T and D, plot by hand your own graph of log T -vs- log D and determine its slope p. Make the scales sufficiently large that the graph occupies a full page. How well does your value for p agree with that determined in the computer analysis?

ii)   According to eqn. 2), the constant k can be determined from either of the two intercepts on this graph. The first intercept, corresponding to log $D = 0$, gives the relation log k = log T. The second intercept, corresponding to log $T = 0$, gives the relation log k = -p log D. Use both intercepts on your graph to obtain two determinations of k. How well do they agree with each other and with the value obtained in step xiii)?

Now express eqn. 1) using your measured values of p and k.

Questions

1. Use your own plot of log *T* -vs- log *D* to determine:

    a) the period of a ring 1 meter in diameter, and
    b) the diameter of a ring having a period of 1 second.

2. A theoretical analysis of the vibrating ring leads to the following equation for the constant *k* in eqn. 1:

$$k = \sqrt{\frac{4\pi^2}{g}}$$

where g is the acceleration due to gravity. Using your measured value for *k*, calculate the value of g. What is the percentage difference between your value and the accepted value for g? Do the two values agree within the range of your experimental uncertainty?

Name: _____   Partner(s):   _____

_____

Table I: *Measured Ring Diameters*

Trial #		Ring Diameters (m)				
		Ring 1	Ring 2	Ring 3	Ring 4	Ring 5
$\bar{d}_o$	1					
	2					
$\bar{d}_o =$						
$\bar{d}_i$	1					
	2					
$\bar{d}_i =$						
$D = (\bar{d}_o + \bar{d}_i)/2$						

Signature of Instructor: _____

Motion in Free-Fall

2

The motion of a body falling freely under gravitational attraction will be examined, and from the measured rate at which the velocity changes with time the acceleration due to gravity (g) will be determined.

Introduction

If a body is acted upon by a net force, then that force causes the body to accelerate. If the force is constant in magnitude, then the acceleration of the body will also be constant. A body which is allowed to fall freely is acted upon by the force of gravitational attraction between that body and the earth, and is directed toward the center of the earth. If the distance of the fall is very much less than the earth's radius then this gravitational force is essentially constant in magnitude and the acceleration due to gravity (g) will be constant during the time of fall. We ignore here a second force due to air resistance, which also acts on a falling body. However, for smooth, dense bodies falling only a short distance, air resistance is very small. Its effect can be ignored in the present experiment.

In Fig. 1 are shown curves representing the relationships between a) displacement and time, and b) velocity and time, for a body moving at constant acceleration. The acceleration is defined as the rate of change of velocity with time; i.e.,

$$a = \frac{v - v_o}{t}$$

$$v = v_0 + at$$

1)

or

where "a" represents the acceleration of the body whose velocity changes from an initial value v_0 to a final value v in the time interval t. From eqn. 1) we see that a plot of v -vs.- t should be a straight line if the acceleration is constant, as seen in Fig. 1(b). *The slope of this line is equal to the acceleration a.* The average velocity of a body is defined as the total displacement (s) travelled by the body divided by the time taken to travel that displacement, i.e.,

$$\bar{v} = \frac{s}{t}$$

2)

For uniformly accelerated motion the average velocity is simply the arithmetic mean of the initial and final velocities (v_0 and v) over the time interval t, i.e.,

$$\bar{v} = \frac{v_0 + v}{2}$$

3)

Furthermore, this average velocity is equal in magnitude to the actual, or instantaneous, velocity midway during the time interval t, i.e., it equals the instantaneous velocity at the instant of time t/2, as can be seen from Fig. 1(b).

Combining now eqns. 1), 2) and 3) we arrive at the following relationship between displacement and time:-

$$s = v_0 t + \frac{1}{2} a t^2$$

4)

From equation 4) we can see that a plot of s -vs.- t should be a parabola if the acceleration is constant, as shown in Fig. 1(a). Also the slope of this parabolic curve at any given instant of time is equal to the velocity of the body at that time. Thus, *the instantaneous velocity of the body at any instant during the motion can be determined by drawing a tangent to the displacement-time curve at the corresponding instant of time and measuring its slope.* Referring again to Fig. 1, the slope of the tangent drawn to the displacement/time curve at the instant t/2 will be equal to the instantaneous velocity of the body at that instant of time, which will also equal the average velocity of the body over the time interval t.

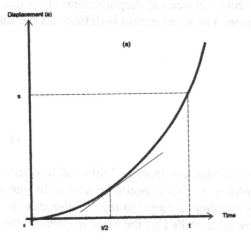 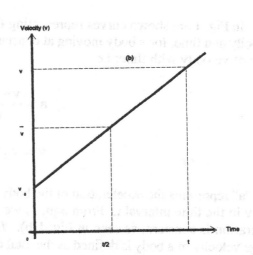

Figure 1: *a) Displacement -vs.- time, and b) velocity -vs.- time curves for uniformly accelerated motion.*

In the present experiment the motion of an object falling freely under gravitational attraction will be studied by measuring its position at various instants of time during the fall. From this the displacement-time and velocity-time graphs can be plotted and the slope of the latter will yield g, the acceleration due to gravity.

The total height through which the weight will fall is about 1.5m, so that it spends only about 0.5 sec. in free-fall (check this for yourself), and all experimental data must be collected in that period of time. Obviously, conventional timing techniques using stop clocks are inadequate for this purpose and other timing methods are necessary.

Procedure

The falling object is a weight attached to a length of paper tape. As the weight falls the tape is drawn through a timer unit comprising a small "hammer" which can be made to vibrate at a frequency of 40 Hz. The hammer will therefore leave a visible mark on the tape at intervals of 1/40th sec. The result is a series of dots in line on the tape representing the position of the weight as a function of time during its fall. From these, the distance traveled can be measured and the average velocity during each time interval can be calculated.

i)   Cut a length of tape about 60 cm long
       from the roll.

ii)   Form a loop at one end and thread the
       other end through the slot of the timer
       unit so that the loop hangs below the
       unit.

iii)   Hold the upper end of the tape with one
       hand and attach a 200g weight from the
       tape loop.

iv)   Switch on the timer unit to 40 Hz
       frequency to start the hammer vibrating
       and then release the tape so that it falls
       freely to the floor.

vi)   Remove the weight from the tape and set
       the tape on the bench surface.

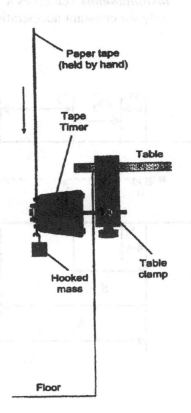

Figure 2. Experimental arrangement of tape timer and tape.

vii)   Your tape should look much like that in Fig. 3. The first few dots are quite close together and should be discarded. Select the first clear dot after this grouping and number this zero. Label the following dots 1, 2, 3, ...etc. to the end of the tape. The dot labeled zero will be considered our origin of both distance and time; i.e. its co-ordinates will be s = 0 and t = 0. All other distances and times will be measured relative to this.

viii) Carefully measure with a meter rule the total distances traveled by the tape from the zeroth dot to succeeding dots (i.e., s_1, s_2, s_3, ...etc. in Fig. 3). Tabulate these against corresponding times, entering the data in the second column of Table 1. (Note that the distance s_1 is traveled in a time 1/40 sec., s_2 in 2/40 sec., s_3 in 3/40 sec., ... etc.)

ix)   With a vernier caliper measure the distances between successive dots (labeled Δs_1, Δs_2, Δs_3,...etc. in Fig. 3). Enter their values in the third column of Table 2. The distances Δs are traveled by the falling weight and tape in equal time intervals of Δt = 1/40 sec.

x)   Calculate the average velocity traveled by the weight and tape during each time interval, i.e.,

$$\bar{v} = \frac{\Delta s}{\Delta t} = 40\Delta s \qquad 5)$$

Enter the values in column 6 of Table 1. These average velocities are equal to the *instantaneous* velocities at the *midpoint* of each corresponding time interval. (This is valid only for constant acceleration, which is true in the present case of free fall.)

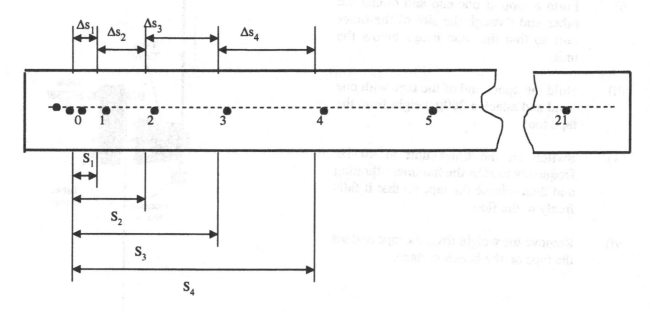

Figure 3. Tape record

Analysis

When plotting the following graphs, be sure to -

1) use graph paper with 10 divisions per cm.,
2) use a fine pencil to plot the data points,
3) circle each data point,
4) chose a scale so that the graph occupies approximately the entire page,
5) label the axes, including the units.

i)   Plot a graph of the **instantaneous velocity -vs.- time** and draw the straight line which best fits all the data points.

ii)   The graph can be represented by the equation for a straight line, i.e.,

$$v = v_0 + at$$

Where v_0 is the initial velocity (the velocity at $t = 0$), and a is the acceleration due to gravity (g). On the graph, v_0 is the intercept on the velocity axis of the v - vs. - t graph and the acceleration a is the slope of the straight line. The slope can be determined from the following procedure:

1) pick two points, A and B, on the plotted straight line,
2) read the coordinate values of v and t at these two points,
3) calculate the slope from:

$$\text{slope} = \frac{v_B - v_A}{t_B - t_A}$$

Determine v_0 and a (i.e., g) from the graph and estimate their uncertainties.

iii)   Plot a graph of the **displacement -vs.- time** (s - vs. - t) and draw a *smooth* curve through the data points.

iv)   In the first half of the motion indicated in the displacement-time curve, select a time interval between two successive data points. In the same manner select another time interval in the second half of the motion. At the mid-point of each time interval draw a tangent to the curve. The slopes of these tangents equal the instantaneous velocities at the chosen instants of time. Measure these slopes and enter their values in Table 2 at the appropriate values of time. How well do these values agree with the corresponding computed values (in column 6 of Table 1)?

Questions

1.   What is the difference between your value of g determined from the velocity-time graph and the accepted value? What do you consider to be the principal sources of experimental uncertainty in your measurement?

2.   If the plummet had been given an initial downward push instead of being released from rest, what effect (if any) would this have on your measured value of g?

3.   From the displacement-time graph what are your conclusions concerning the dependence of displacement on time for a body in free-fall? What is the functional relationship between displacement and time for this motion?

4.   Should the tangent to your displacement-time curve at the point selected to be s = 0 and t = 0 be horizontal? Explain your answer carefully.

Name: _____   Partner(s):   _____

_____

n =   dot number
s_n =   distance from n^{th} dot to 0th dot, measured with meter stick
Δs_n =   distance between n^{th} and $(n-1)^{th}$ dot, measured with vernier caliper
Δt =   time interval (= $1/40^{th}$ sec.)

Table 1: Experimental Data

n	$t = n\Delta t$ (s)	s_n [1] (cm)	Δs_n [2] (cm)	t (at midpoint) (s)	$v = \Delta s_n / \Delta t$ (cm/s)
0	0	0	--------------	----------------	--------------
1					
2					

[1] Estimated uncertainty in   s = _____ cm
[2] Estimated uncertainty in Δs = _____ cm

Table 2: Instantaneous Velocities

t (at midpoint) (s)	v* (cm/s)	v (from Table 1) (cm/s)

* Determined from slopes of tangents to the s -vs.- t graph.

Signature of Instructor: _____

Conservation Laws
in 1-D Collisions

3

The roles of momentum and kinetic energy in various one-dimensional collisions will be examined.

Introduction

A. Conservation Laws:

In this experiment collisions occur between two gliders moving on a horizontal airtrack. Since frictional forces on an air track are very small and the gravitational force has no horizontal component, the external forces acting horizontally on the gliders are negligible. Under this condition, the law of conservation of momentum requires that the total momentum **p** (= mv) of the two gliders remains constant in the horizontal direction and, therefore, must be the same before and after a collision. We may express this law in terms of the initial and final momenta of the system as follows:

$$\mathbf{p}_i = \mathbf{p}_f$$

$$\text{where} \quad \mathbf{p}_i = \mathbf{p}_{1i} + \mathbf{p}_{2i} \quad = \text{total initial momentum before collision}$$

$$\text{and} \quad \mathbf{p}_f = \mathbf{p}_{1f} + \mathbf{p}_{2f} \quad = \text{total final momentum after collision}$$

The subscripts 1 and 2 refer to Glider #1 and Glider #2, respectively. Since momentum is a vector quantity the rules of vector addition apply, so proper attention must be paid to the directions of motion.

The different types of collisions which may occur between two bodies can be classified according to the affect a collision has on either their relative velocity or their total kinetic energy. If the magnitude of the relative velocity is unchanged by a collision then that collision is said to be *elastic*. If its magnitude is greater after a collision then the collision is *explosive*, and if less the collision is described as *inelastic*. In the special case where the relative velocity is zero after the collision (i.e., the two bodies stay together, moving as one after the collision), the collision is said to be *totally inelastic*.

The total kinetic energy K of the system (=½mv^2) before and after collision can be expressed as:

$$K_i = K_{1i} + K_{2i} = \text{total initial k.e. before collision}$$

$$\text{and} \quad K_i = K_{1i} + K_{2i} = \text{total final k.e. after collision}$$

Since kinetic energy is a scalar quantity, then simple scalar addition applies.

In an elastic collision the total kinetic energy of the system also remains unchanged, i.e., $K_i = K_f$. If, however, the collision is inelastic, there is a net loss of kinetic energy (i.e., $K_f < K_i$), with the greatest possible loss occurring in a totally inelastic collision.

To summarize, if no *net* external force acts on a system, the total momentum of the system is conserved in all classes of collision, whereas the total kinetic energy is conserved only if a collision is elastic. In this experiment the momenta and kinetic energies will be measured for two gliders which undergo several different elastic and totally inelastic collisions.

B. Method:

The general arrangement is shown in Figure 1. The two gliders have masses m_1 and m_2 and lengths ℓ_1 and ℓ_2, respectively. Their initial velocities before a collision (v_{1i} and v_{2i}) and final velocities after the collision (v_{1f} and v_{2f}) are determined by measuring the times taken for each glider to pass through one or other of two photogates (represented by G_1 and G_2 in the figure) before and after collision and calculating ℓ/t for each pass. These time intervals are measured by a computer to which the photogates are interfaced. The computer also analyses each collision and the results can be printed for inclusion in your report.

By using different attachments on the ends of the gliders, both elasic and totally inelastic collisions can be studied. Collisions between different masses can also be examined by adding weights to the gliders.

In Fig. 2 are depicted four different conditions for the gliders before collision. The first three involve collisions between gliders of equal or unequal masses in which Glider #2 (m_2) is initially at rest and is struck by Glider #1 (m_1). In the fourth case both gliders are shown moving before collision. All four cases will be examined (and any others you want to try), first with elastic collisions and then repeated for totally inelastic collisions. Since velocities and momenta are vector quantities proper account must be taken of their directions in analyzing a collision. The computer takes the positive vector direction to be that of v_{1i}, the direction of the initial velocity of m_1, and m_1 is always taken to be that glider which passes through Gate #1 *before* the collision.

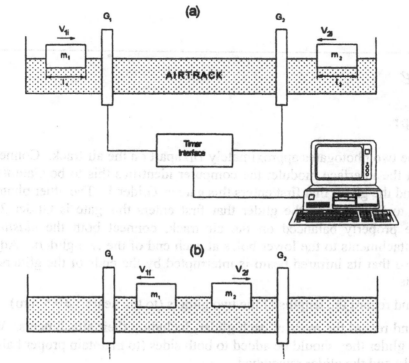

Figure 1: Gliders m_1 and m_2 moving on the air track a) before collision, and b) shortly after collision.

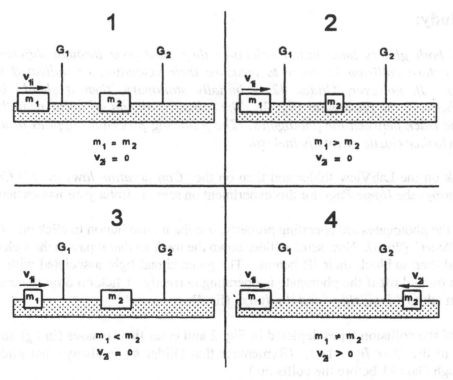

Figure 2: Four different initial conditions are depicted for collision between two gliders. These will be studied for both elastic and totally inelastic collisions.

Procedure

A. Initial Setup:

i)   Position the two photogates approximately 1m apart on the air track. Connect one of them to Port #1 on the interface module; the computer identifies this to be Gate #1 in the collision analyses and the glider that first enters this gate as Glider 1. The other photogate, Gate #2, is connected to Port #2 and the glider that first enters this gate is Glider 2. To ensure the gliders are properly balanced on the air track, connect both the *elastic-* **and** *inelastic-collision* attachments to the lower holes at each end of the two gliders. Adjust the height of each gate so that its infrared beam is interrupted by the ends of the gliders and not by their attachments.

ii)   Measure and record the lengths of the two gliders (to the nearest ±0.5 mm).

iii)   Measure and record the mass of each glider, including their attachments. When weights are added to a glider they should be added to both sides (to maintain proper balance of the glider on the track) and the glider reweighed.

iv)   Turn on the air supply and wait about 10 minutes before carefully leveling the track.

B. Collisions Study:

NOTE: If both gliders have initial velocities they must pass through different photogates before collision in order to measure their velocities, as indicated in Figure 1(a). If, however, Glider #2 is initially stationary, then it should be positioned between the photogates (fig. 2). The collisions should all occur near the center of the track between the photogates. The following procedure applies to all collisions, whether elastic or totally inelastic.

v)   Double click on the LabView folder and then on the *"Conservation laws in 1D-Collisions"* icon. This brings the *Home Page* for this experiment on screen. Enter your names here.

vi)   To test that the photogates are operating properly, use the mouse button to click on *"Photogate Test"* then *"Start"* (fig. 3). Now send a glider down the track so that it passes through each gate to block and then unblock their IR beams. The green signal light associated with each gate should flash on and off if the photogate is operating correctly. Click on *Stop* to conclude the test and then tab to *"Acquisition and Analysis"* (fig.4).

vii)   Select one of the collision types depicted in Fig. 2 and enter their masses (in kg) and lengths (in meters) in the *User Input* box. (Remember that Glider #1 is always that glider which passes through Gate #1 before the collision.)

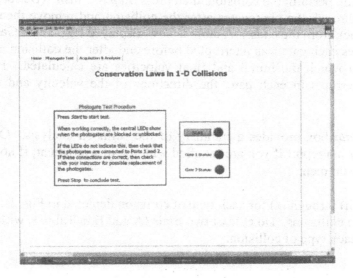

Figure 3. Photogates test screen

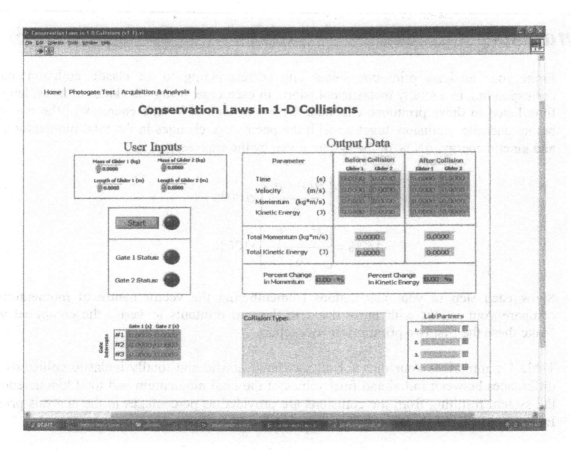

Figure 4: Acquisition and Analysis screen.

viii)   Press *Start* again, perform the collision, then press ***Stop*** to finish. (Be sure **both** gliders complete their passage through the photogates after the collision and remove them from the track before they bounce back from the ends.) A table is now displayed (fig. 3) for Gates 1 and 2 showing the number of times each gate was interrupted before and after the collision and the duration of each interrupt, from which the initial and final velocities are calculated. From the sequence and number of interrupts in each gate, the directions of the velocity and momentum vectors are determined.

ix)   The *Output Data* box provides a summary of the collision analysis. Obtain a printout of this screen for your lab report if you are satisfied with the measurement; if not, return to step vii) and repeat the measurement.

x)   Repeat steps vii) through ix) for each type of collision depicted in Fig. 2, and for both elastic and totally inelastic collisions. Do at least two trials (A and B in Table I) with different initial velocities for each type of collision.

Analysis

i)   From your analysis printouts, select one corresponding to an elastic collision and one corresponding to a totally inelastic collision. In each case, using the values of mass, length and time listed in those printouts, calculate the momenta and kinetic energies of the two gliders before and after collision, together with the percentage changes in the total momentum, $\Delta p\%$, and kinetic energy, $\Delta K\%$, of the system given by the expressions:

$$\Delta p\% = \left[\frac{p_f - p_i}{p_i} \right] x100\%$$

$$\Delta K\% = \left[\frac{K_f - K_i}{K_i} \right] x100\%$$

Show each step in your calculations (remembering the vector nature of momentum) and compare your values with those listed in the two printouts to verify the computed values. Make these the first two printouts in your report.

ii)   Table I summarizes your data for all measured elastic and totally inelastic collisions. Any differences between initial and final values of the total momentum and total kinetic energy of the system resulting from the collisions are provided as percentages in the analysis printouts. Enter into the table all computed values of $\Delta p\%$ and $\Delta K\%$ from these printouts.

iii)   Calculate the overall average % change in momentum for the collisions. (**NOTE:** You may exclude from this average those cases in which both gliders were moving toward one another before collision.)

Calculate also the average % change in kinetic energy for the elastic collisions.

In your report discuss carefully the extent to which your measurements support, within the experimental uncertainties, the law of conservation of momentum in all types of collisions and the conservation of kinetic energy in the case of elastic collisions.

iv)   In those cases involving totally inelastic collisions *in which Glider #2 (m₂) is initially at rest*, the loss in kinetic energy can be predicted and is given by the relation:

$$\Delta K\% = -\left[\frac{m_2}{m_1 + m_2}\right] x100\% \quad \text{(for totally inelastic collisions and } v_{2i} = 0)$$

Calculate this value for all totally inelastic collisions studied and enter the corresponding values in the last column of Table I. How well do your predicted and measured losses in kinetic energy agree?

Questions

1.   Do your data support the statement in the Introduction that the relative velocity remains unchanged in an elastic collision? Justify your answer by comparing the relative velocities before and after collision for the four elastic cases for which you have printouts.

2.   A glider of mass 0.15 kg is directed toward the end-stop of an air track with a velocity of 1.2 ms⁻¹ and is observed to recoil with the same speed. If the collision with the end-stop lasted just 0.01s, what average force was exerted on the glider during the collision?

Name: _____   Partner(s): _____

_____

Table I: *Measured Changes in the Initial and Final Total Momentum and Total Kinetic Energy in Elastic and Inelastic Collisions*

Collision Type E = Elastic I = Inelestic	L1 = (m) m_1 (kg)	L2 = (m) m_2 (kg)	Momentum and Kinetic Energy Changes $\Delta p\%$	$\Delta K\%$	$\dfrac{-m_2}{m_1 + m_2} \times 100\%$ *
1E A					
B					
2E A					
B					
3E A					
B					
4E A					
B					
Average % Change					
1I A					
B					
2I A					
B					
3I A					
B					
4I A					
B					
Average % Change					

* Percentage loss in kinetic energy for a totally inelastic collision when $v_{2i} = 0$.

Signature of Instructor: _____

Conservation of Momentum: The Ballistic Pendulum

4

The laws governing momentum and mechanical energy in a totally inelastic collision will be examined using a ballistic pendulum.

Introduction

When two bodies collide they exert equal and opposing forces on each other and, in the absence of any externally applied forces, they experience equal and opposite changes of momentum. The total momentum of the system (i.e of the two bodies) therefore remains constant throughout the collision. This is the ***law of conservation of momentum***. In this experiment the two bodies adhere after impact, a form of collision called ***totally inelastic***. In this event, although momentum is conserved, the kinetic energy of the system is not, the latter being dissipitated in the form of heat, inelastic deformation, etc.

The apparatus (see Fig. 1) comprises a pendulum and a spring gun for propelling a projectile. The pendulum consists of a heavy bob hollowed out to receive the projectile and is suspended by a light metal rod which is pivoted at its upper end. The projectile is a small steel sphere which, when fired into the pendulum bob, becomes captured there. A marker on the side of the bob indicates the position of the center_of_mass of the pendulum-projectile system. After the projectile is fired into the pendulum bob, the pendulum swings upward in an arc and the angle corresponding to the maximum height reached by the center-of-mass can be read with a protractor. The steel projectile ball may be released by the spring gun with three different initial velocities.

Suppose the projectile, having a mass m and initial velocity u, is fired horizontally into the pendulum of mass M, which is initially hanging at rest in the vertical position (Fig. 2a). As a result of this collision, the pendulum bob with the projectile inside is given a velocity v (Fig. 2b). Since the external gravitational force acts only vertically, momentum in the horizontal direction will be preserved providing the collision process is completed (and the final velocity v is reached) before the pendulum has any significant opportunity to swing upwards. This condition is satisfied providing M » m.

From momentum conservation we can write:

$$p_i = p_f \qquad\qquad\qquad\qquad\qquad\qquad\qquad\qquad\qquad\qquad 1)$$

where $p_i = mu$ is the total initial momentum of the system before collision and $p_f = mv + Mv$ is the total final momentum immediately after collision. Therefore,

$$mu = (m + M)v \qquad\qquad\qquad\qquad\qquad\qquad\qquad\qquad 2)$$

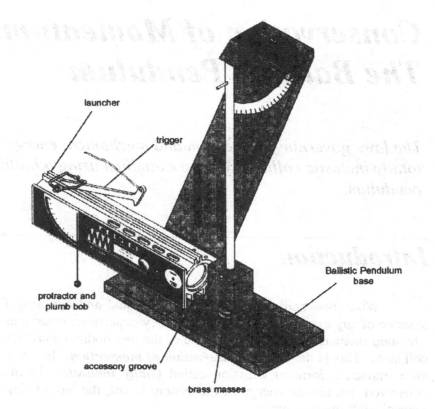

Figure 1. *Ballistic Pendulum*

launcher

trigger

Ballistic Pendulum
base

protractor and
plumb bob

accessory groove

brass masses

It is this equality expressed in eqn. 2) and predicted by the law of conservation of momentum which we wish to test in the experiment. To do so, it is necessary to determine the initial and final velocities u and v through independent measurements.

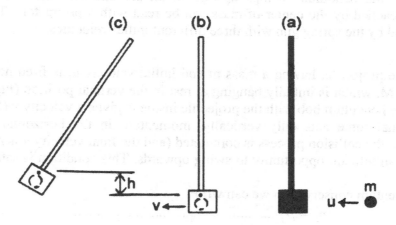

Figure 2: *Configuration of the pendulum/projectile system (a) before the collision, (b) immediately after the collision, and (c) when the system has reached its maximum height.*

i) Determination of u

The initial velocity u of the projectile shot horizontally from the spring gun can be determined by measuring its range x when allowed to fall freely under gravity through a height 'y' (Fig. 3).

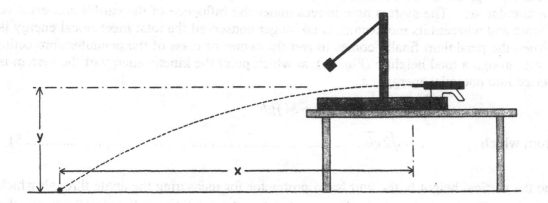

Figure 3: *Measurement of projectile velocity, u.*

In a time interval t the projectile will fall vertically through a distance:

$$y = \frac{1}{2}gt^2$$

and in the same time interval its horizontal displacement is just:

$$x = ut$$

Eliminating t and solving for u we have:

$$u = x\sqrt{\frac{g}{2y}} \quad \dots\dots\dots\dots 3)$$

The initial momentum of the system before the collision can therefore be expressed in the form:

$$p_i = mx\sqrt{\frac{g}{2y}} \quad \dots\dots\dots\dots 4)$$

ii) Determination of v

NOTE: *The following derivation for v is only approximately valid since rotational energy and angular momentum of the pendulum system are not taken into account. However, their inclusion will not greatly change the numerical results for this system.*

The velocity v given to the pendulum bob immediately following the collision causes it to swing along a circular arc. The system now moves under the influence of the earth's conservative gravitational force and whereas its momentum is no longer conserved the total mechanical energy is conserved. When the pendulum finally comes to rest the center of mass of the pendulum/projectile system has risen through a total height h (Fig. 2c), at which point the kinetic energy of the system is entirely converted into potential energy, i.e.,

$$\frac{1}{2}(m+M)v^2 = (m+M)gh$$

from which $\qquad v = \sqrt{2gh}$ .... 5)

To determine the vertical height h, the unit has a protractor for measuring the angle through which the pendulum swings. By measuring the initial angle θ_i when the pendulum is hanging freely and the final angle θ_f after it reaches its maximum height, h can be determined from $(\theta_f - \theta_i)$ and is given by:

$$h = L_{cm}\left[1 - \cos(\theta_f - \theta_i)\right]$$

where L_{cm} is the length of the pendulum to its center-of-mass. The length and mass for this unit are:

$$L_{cm} = 0.27 \text{ m} \; ; \quad M = 0.240 \text{ kg}$$

With the height measured, the final momentum of the system immediately after the collision can be expressed in the form:

$$p_f = (m+M)\sqrt{2gh}$$ .... 6)

The measured values of and can now be compared to test the law of conservation of momentum expressed in eqn. 1).

iii) Energy Loss in the Collision

The loss of kinetic energy in the system resulting from the collision can be independently predicted. Before the collision we have:

$$K_i = \frac{1}{2}mu^2$$ .... 7)

Immediately after the collision the final kinetic energy is:

$$K_f = \frac{1}{2}(m+M)v^2$$ .... 8)

From conservation of momentum (eqn. 2), we can also write K_f in terms of u, i.e.,

$$K_f = \frac{1}{2}\frac{m^2}{(m+M)}u^2 \quad\dotfill 9)$$

The fractional loss in kinetic energy $\Delta K/K_i$ is:

$$\frac{\Delta K}{K_i} = \frac{K_i - K_f}{K_i} = 1 - \frac{K_f}{K_i}$$

From equations 7) and 9) we have:

$$\frac{K_f}{K_i} = \frac{m}{m+M}$$

The fractional loss in kinetic energy can therefore be expressed in the form:

$$\frac{\Delta K}{K_i} = \frac{M}{m+M} \quad\dotfill 10)$$

According to eqn. 10), we see that the loss in kinetic energy of the system resulting from the collision is determined entirely by the masses of the projectile and pendulum and independent of the velocities involved.

Procedure

CAUTION: *never look directly into the barrel. The steel projectile might be loaded in the barrel and not be readily seen from the outside.*

i)   Use the plumb line to level the unit.

ii)   Measure the mass of the steel projectile ball and record this in the data sheet.

iii)   A ramrod is provided to load the projectile ball into the barrel and a "click" is heard each time the ball passes one of the three range settings. Only one "click" is heard when the ball is positioned for the *short range* projection, two clicks for the *mid-range*, and three for the *long range*. Position the ball for the *long range* and retrieve the ramrod slowly so the ball remains properly seated.

iv)   Position the angle indicator against the pin and record the angle (θ_i). Release the projectile so that it is captured by the pendulum bob and record the final angle (θ_f) of the pendulum. Record the change in angle ($\theta_f - \theta_i$). Repeat this for three measurements. The change in angle should be very reproducible for the same range providing the ball was properly seated in the barrel. Determine the average change in angle ($\theta_f - \theta_i$) and use this average to determine h in Table I. (Exclude any outlier values that may occur due, for example, to an improperly seated projectile.)

v)   Repeat steps iii) and iv) for the mid-range and short range, recording your average values for ($\theta_f - \theta_i$) in the appropriate row of Table 1.

---

vi)   Position the pendulum at the top of its swing (it will snap into a holder and remain out of the way).

vii)   Place the unit near the edge of the lab bench to provide about two meters of "firing" range across the floor. Use the plumb line to check that the unit is again level.

viii)   Make trial firings for both long and short ranges, using some convenient backstop to retrieve the ball, and note where the ball strikes the floor each time. Cover this full range with fan-fold paper and tape the paper to the floor with just two pieces of tape (so that it can be quickly removed without damage).

ix)   Make four successive firings on the long range. A small indentation is left on the paper at each point of contact. Use a pen to mark the centers of these indentations.

x)   Measure the average range $\bar{x}$ (i.e., the horizontal distance between the initial position of the projectile as it leaves the barrel and the centroid of the four marks) and record this in Table II.

xi)   Repeat steps ix) and x) for both the mid- and the short-range settings, recording your results in the appropriate row of Table II.

xii)   Measure and record the height 'y' through which the ball falls (from the bottom of the ball when mounted on the barrel to the floor).

Analysis

i)   Calculate the velocity v of the projectile/pendulum system after the collision, its final momentum p_f, and its final kinetic energy K_f, for all three cases of short-, mid- and long-range (see Table I).

ii)   Calculate for all three ranges the initial velocity u, momentum p_i, and kinetic energy K_i of the system before collision (Table II).

iii)   Calculate the percentage changes in momentum and kinetic energy (Table III). Calculate also the expected change in kinetic energy based on the masses alone (last column of Table III).

Be sure to include in your Discussion whether your measured percentage changes in momentum are consistent with the law of conservation of momentum. Also, how well do the measured percentage changes in kinetic energy compare with the values predicted from eqn. 10?

Questions

1.   If the collision between the projectile and pendulum had lasted 1 millisecond, what would the average force have been which the projectile exerted on the pendulum for the long-range case?

2.   How much work did you do (in joules) in compressing the spring of the spring gun for the long-range case? Which law of conservation is your answer based upon?

3.   If the measurements were repeated in an area where $g = 5$ m.s^{-2}, what changes if any would you observe in a) the height through which the pendulum rises after impact, and b) the range of the projectile? Would your values for the momentum and kinetic energy differ from the present measurements? Explain your answers carefully.

Name: _____   Partner(s): _____

_____

Experimenta Data and Analysis

Mass of Pendulum, $M =$ 0.240   kg
Mass of Projectile, $m =$ kg
Total mass, $(M + m) =$ kg

Initial angle $\theta_i =$ degrees

Table I. Determination of Final Momentum and Kinetic Energy

Range	$\theta_f - \theta_i$ (degrees)	$h = 0.27\,[1-\cos(\theta_f - \theta_i)]$ (meters)	$v = (2gh)^{1/2}$ (m/s)	$p_f = (m+M)v$ (kg.m/s)	$K_f = \frac{1}{2}(m+M)v^2$ (joules)
Long					
Medium					
Short					

Table II. Determination of Initial Momentum and Kinetic Energy

Range	x (meters)	y (meters)	$u = x(g/2y)^{1/2}$ (m/s)	$p_i = mu$ (kg.m/s)	$K_i = \frac{1}{2}mu^2$ (joules)
Long					
Medium					
Short					

Signature of Instructor: _____

Name: _____   Partner(s):   _____

_____

Table III. *Changes in Momentum and Kinetic Energy*

Range	p_i (kg.m/s)	p_f (kg.m/s)	$\dfrac{\Delta p}{p_i}$ x100%	K_i (joules)	K_f (joules)	$\dfrac{\Delta K}{K_i}$ x100%	$\dfrac{M}{m+M}$ x100%
Long							
Medium							
Short							

Signature of Instructor: _____

Rotational Motion *5*

By applying known torques to a system which is free to rotate, the resulting angular acceleration will be measured and used to determine the moment of inertia of the system.

Introduction

The laws which govern rotational motion follow from Newton's laws just as do those which govern linear motion. If an object is rotating about a fixed axis, then Newton's law describing its rotational motion can be expressed as,

$$\tau = I\alpha \quad \text{...} 1)$$

where τ is the net *moment of force*, or *torque*, about the axis which results in an *angular acceleration*, α, and I is the *moment of inertia* (sometimes called *rotational inertia*) of the object about the axis. The moment of inertia is, therefore, a measure of the tendency of the object to resist a change in its rotational motion, analogous to mass in linear motion.

The moment of inertia of a small element of mass, m, rotating about an axis distance r away (Fig. 1), is just mr^2. The moment of inertia of an extended rigid body, on the other hand, depends on the way in which its mass is distributed relative to the axis of rotation. Such a body can be thought of as made up of a very large number of elemental masses and the total moment of inertia is then the sum of contributions from all such masses (Fig. 2). If m_i represents the mass of one such element located at a distance r_i from the axis, then the total moment of inertia can be written as:

$$I = \sum_{i=1}^{N} m_i r_i^2 \quad \text{...} 2)$$

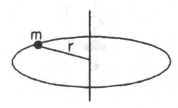

Figure 1. *Small mass rotating about axis has moment of inertia mr^2.*

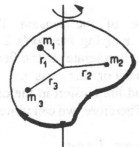

Figure 2. *Extended rigid body rotating about an axis.*

where N is sufficiently large that each mass element approximates a point mass. When the shape of a rotating body is simple and symmetric, I can usually be calculated in a straightforward manner. However, it can also be measured experimentally by application of eqn. 1, and this is often the easier method of determining I if the body is irregularly shaped. Thus, if a known torque is applied to a body and the resulting angular acceleration is measured, then the moment of inertia is just $I = \tau / \alpha$. We shall examine this method in the present investigation.

The apparatus comprises a heavy wooden platter with a small cylindrical spindle of radius "r" at its center. The latter is used to mount the platter on a small table and to rotate it about an axis through the center. The general arrangement is shown in Figure 3. A cord is wrapped around the center spindle and passes over a pulley in the manner shown. When a weight of mass m is suspended from the cord and allowed to fall, the tension (T) in the cord applies a torque τ to the spindle causing the platter to rotate with an angular acceleration α, which can be readily determined from the linear acceleration "a" of the falling weight. The photogate is used for timing measurements.

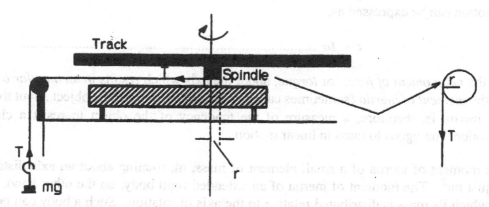

Figure 3. *Experimental arrangement for determining moment of inertia.*

The torque applied to the system by the tension in the cord is given by the moment of the tension about the axis, i.e.,

$$\tau = Tr \quad \text{.. 3)}$$

The magnitude of the tension T can be determined by applying Newton's 2nd law to the mass m as it accelerates to the floor (Figure 4). Two forces act on this mass, the weight mg acting down and the tension in the cord acting vertically up. Therefore, we can write:

$$mg - T = ma$$

Figure 4. *Forces Acting on mass, m*

from which:

$$T = m(g - a) \quad \text{.. 4)}$$

Combining eqns. 1, 3 and 4, we have,

$$m(g - a)r - \tau_f = I\alpha \quad\text{...} 5)$$

In eqn. 5 we have also allowed for the possibility of some frictional torque, τ_f, acting in the system which opposes the applied torque $m(g - a)r$, and so reduces the angular acceleration.

The linear and angular accelerations are not independent of one another but are related through

$$a = \alpha r \quad\text{..} 6)$$

so eqn. 5 can be expressed in terms of α only, i.e.,

$$m(g - \alpha r)r = I\alpha + \tau_f \quad\text{..} 7)$$

Equation 7) predicts that a plot of the applied torque, $m(g - \alpha r)r$, versus the angular acceleration, α, will yield a straight line with slope I and an intercept equal to the frictional torque acting in the system.

Procedure

Various torques will be applied to the system using different suspended masses, m. A disk containing multiple slits rotates with the platter and the slits periodically interrupt the infrared beam of a photogate interfaced with a computer. The computer records the time intervals between successive interrupts and, by knowing the angular displacement between the slits, computes the average angular velocities between interrupts. From these, the angular acceleration can be determined for each applied torque (or hanging mass).

NOTE: Include in your lab report printouts of the "Summary Table" and "Frictional Analysis" pages, and just two examples of the "Data Acquisition" and "Kinematic Curves" pages.

i)   Measure and record in Table I the mass (**M**) of the platter, its diameter (**D**), and the radius of the central spindle (**r**).

ii)   Double click on the LabView folder and then on the *"Rotational Motion"* icon. This brings the *Home Page* for this experiment on screen. Enter your names here.

iii)   Set the platter rotating and with the mouse button click on *"Photogate Test"* then *Start*. The green signal light should flash on and off if the photogate is operating correctly. Click on *Stop*.

iv)   Wind the cord around the center spindle of the system, in one layer if possible and in regular turns so there will be no interference as the cord unwinds.

v)   Pass the cord over the pulley and attach a small mass (e.g., 30g plus hanger) to its free end (Fig. 3). Keep the mass supported at this point. Select the *"Data Acquisition"* page (Fig. 4) and enter in the control box the mass m in kg (including 5g for the mass of the hanger).

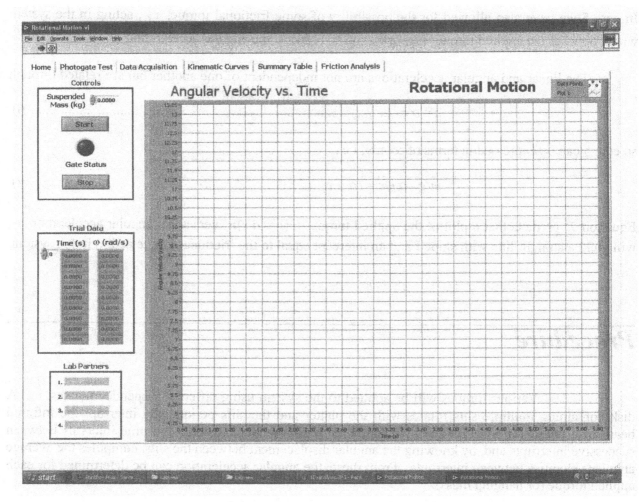

Figure 4. Data Acquisition Page

vi)   Release the mass and after one rotation click the **BEGIN** data collection button. Press **END** well before the mass strikes the floor and stop the platter rotating. The computer measures the time intervals (Δt) between successive interruptions of a photogate whenever the platter rotates through a certain angular displacement of $\Delta\theta$ radians. From these the average angular velocity ($\omega = \Delta\theta / \Delta t$ rads.s^{-1}) is computed during each displacement interval $\Delta\theta$. It then provides a graph of this angular velocity as a function of time, fitted with a straight line which best fits the data. The slope of this line is equal to the angular acceleration of the mass during its descent. A pop-up window appears allowing you to choose whether or not to accept this measurement.

vii) If *"Kinematic Curves"* is selected now (Fig. 5), a set of graphs are shown of the principal kinematic quantities corresponding to this mass: angular displacement –vs.- time, angular acceleration –vs.- time, and angular velocity –vs.- time.

viii) Repeat steps ii) through v) for about ten other masses in 10g steps (e.g., 45g, 55g, …etc.). Include in your laboratory report printouts for just two sets of the kinematic curves as examples.

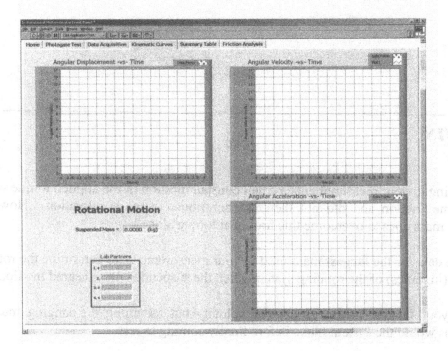

Figure 5. *Kinematic Curves of Rotational Motion*

x)   The frictional torque can be measured independently as follows. Wrap the cord completely around the center spindle and start the platter spinning near the fastest rate observed during the previous measurements. Select *"Frictional Analysis"* and click **BEGIN** button. Record measurements for about 100 rotations. A graph of the angular velocity –vs.- time will be displayed and the slope of the straight line which best fits the data (equal to the angular deceleration, α') will be shown. Print this graph for your report.

Analysis

i)   Using the summary table in step ix) above, calculate the applied torque for each mass (see Table II). Plot **by hand** a graph of applied torque -vs.- angular acceleration. (This graph must have a true origin (0,0) to produce a y-intercept.) From this graph, determine the moment of inertia of the system from the slope and the frictional torque from the intercept (see eqn. 7).

ii)   The moment of inertia I of a disc having mass M and radius R is $\frac{1}{2}MR^2$. Calculate this value for the platter and compare it with the value obtained from the slope in i). How well do they agree?

iii) From your measured angular deceleration (α') in step x) above, and using the measured value of I determined above, estimate the frictional torque in the system using the relationship $\tau_f = I\alpha'$. How well does this agree with the value determined in step (i) above?

Questions

1.   According to your measurements a small constant portion of the applied torque was required to overcome friction and did not therefore contribute to the acceleration. How much of the applied mass goes to overcome this frictional torque alone?

2.   Use the data for the **largest** mass used in your measurements to determine the rotational kinetic energy (in joules) of the rotating system when the suspended mass neared the floor.

3.   Using your **largest** measured angular velocity but assuming no hanging mass, how many rotations would the system make before finally coming to rest.

Name: _____   Partner(s):   _____

                                                            _____

Table I: *Data for Moment of Inertia Calculation*

Radius of spindle,   r = _____ meter

Mass of Platter,   M = _____ kg

Diameter of Platter,   D = _____ meter

($\therefore$ Radius of Platter, R = _____ meter)

I_{disk} ($= \frac{1}{2}MR^2$) = _____ kg.m^2

Table II: *Data for Moment of Inertia Measurement*

Applied Mass m (kg)	Angular Acceleration α (rads.s^{-2})	Cord Tension $T = m(g - \alpha r)$ (N)	Applied Torque $\tau = Tr$ (N.m)

Signature of Instructor: _____

Some Properties of Fluids

6

Behaviours of static and moving fluids are studied through a set of experiments based on Archimedes Principle, the Equation of Continuity, and Bernoulli's equation.

Introduction

Several aspects of fluid behavior will be explored in this set of four experiments chosen to demonstrate Archimedes Principle, Pascal's Principle, the Equation of Continuity, and Bernoulli's Equation.

Archimedes principle states that a body immersed in a fluid is buoyed up by a force equal to the weight of the displaced fluid. In the first experiment, this principle is applied to irregular solid objects that are heavier than water to determine their volume, their density, and ultimately their composition.

In a second experiment, Archimedes principle is applied to a floating object to verify that the mass of the displaced water equals the mass of the floating object.

Pascal's principle states that a change in pressure applied to an enclosed incompressible fluid is transmitted undiminished throughout the fluid and to the walls of the container. In a third experiment, this principle is applied to a hydraulic jack. The total mechanical advantage of the jack is the product of the hydraulic mechanical advantage and the mechanical advantage of the lever pumping arm. This produces such a large mechanical advantage in a very compact device that objects weighing many tons can be lifted by hand.

The equation of continuity and Bernoulli's equation are useful in describing fluids in motion. They are derived from mass conservation and energy conservation, respectively. In a fourth experiment, the velocity of water out of a small hole near the bottom of a container filled with water is calculated based on these equations and compared to the velocity derived from projectile motion. Bernoulli's equation ignores the frictional effects of viscosity and therefore gives only an approximate result.

Archimedes' Principle

Uniform solid object heavier than water completely submerged in water (see fig. 1).

Archimedes' principle states that a body immersed in a fluid is buoyed up by a force equal to the weight of the displaced fluid. In this case, the volume of the displaced fluid equals the volume of the object. By measuring the object's volume and mass, its density and composition can be determined.

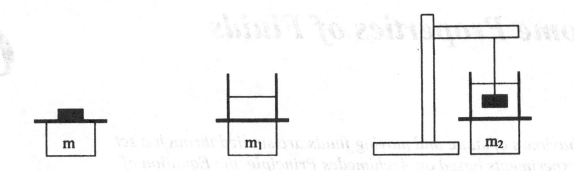

Figure 1. *Apparatus for Archimedes' Principle*

Object's weight in air = mg
Object's apparent weight when submerged in water = m'g
Weight of the displaced water = $m_w g = \rho_w V_{object} g$

$$mg - m'g = m_w g$$

$$\Delta m = m - m' = \rho_w V_{object}, \qquad \textbf{where } \rho_w \textbf{ is the density of water}$$

$$V_{object} = \Delta m / \rho_w \quad ....1)$$

$$\rho_{object} = m / V_{object} \quad ....2)$$

The mass difference is determined from the measurements depicted in the figure above.

$$\Delta m = m_2 - m_1 \quad ....3)$$

(Eqn. 3 is useful since scales read in terms of mass.)

Uniform solid object lighter than water floating at its surface.

Archimedes' principle applied to this case equates the weight of the displaced water to the weight of the floating object. Hence, by measuring the volume of the displaced fluid and multiplying by its density and acceleration due to gravity, a weight equal to that of the floating object is determined.

$$m_{object} g = \rho_w V_w g$$

$$m_{object} = \rho_w V_w \quad ....4)$$

Pascal's principle

Operation of a Hydraulic Jack.

Pascal's principle states that a change in pressure applied to an enclosed incompressible fluid is transmitted undiminished throughout the fluid and to the walls of the container. This pressure change is therefore the same for a small piston as for a large piston. This can be demonstrated using a hydraulic jack, depicted in fig.2.

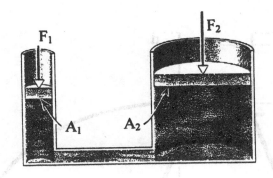

Figure 2. *Principle of the Hydraulic Jack.*

Referring to fig. 2,

$$\Delta p = F_1/A_1 = F_2/A_2$$

Hydraulic mechanical advantage in terms of the piston areas

$$(MA)_{hydr.} = F_2/F_1 = A_2/A_1$$

or in terms of the piston diameters

$$(MA)_{hydr.} = (d_2/d_1)^2 \quad ....5)$$

The mechanical advantage derived from the pumping arm with lever distances L_2 and L_1

$$(MA)_{arm} = L_2/L_1 \quad ....6)$$

Total mechanical advantage

$$(MA)_{total} = (MA)_{hydr.} \times (MA)_{arm} \quad ....7)$$

Hence the force achieved (F_2) from that applied (F_1) is

$$F_2 = (MA)_{total} \times F_1 \quad ....8)$$

Bernoulli's equation

Consider water flowing out of a small hole near the bottom of a container filled with water (see fig. 3). Relating the water at the surface (designated 1) to the water escaping the hole (designated 2) and using Bernoulli's equation:

$$p_1 + \rho g y_1 + \tfrac{1}{2} \rho v_1^2 = p_2 + \rho g y_2 + \tfrac{1}{2} \rho v_2^2$$

The continuity equation will show that the third term in this expression is negligible.

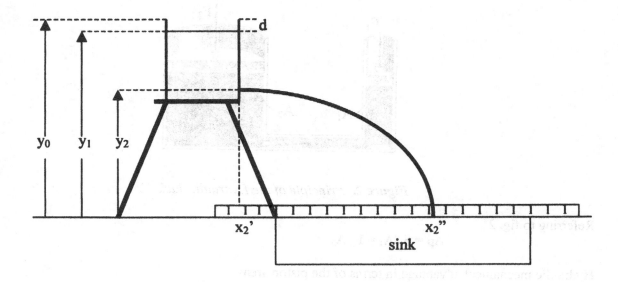

Figure 3. *Water Flowing from Hole in a Container.*

$$A_1 v_1 = A_2 v_2$$

$$v_1 = (A_2/A_1)v_2$$

Hence, $v_1 << v_2$

In addition to dropping the third term, both pressures equal atmospheric pressure, hence they cancel one another. Solving for v_2

$$v_2 = [2 \, g \, (y_1 - y_2)]^{1/2} \quad \dots\dots\dots\dots\dots\dots\dots\dots\dots\dots\dots\dots\dots\dots\dots\dots\dots\dots\dots\dots\dots 9)$$

Treating the stream of water as projectile motion also gives the velocity at the hole.

For motion in the x direction:

$$x_2 = v_2 \, t_f$$

For motion in the y direction:

$$y = y_2 - \tfrac{1}{2} \, g \, t_f^2 = 0$$

$$y_2 = \tfrac{1}{2} \, g \, (x_2/v_2)^2$$

$$v_2 = x_2(g/2y_2)^{1/2} \quad \dots\dots\dots\dots\dots\dots\dots\dots\dots\dots\dots\dots\dots\dots\dots\dots\dots\dots\dots\dots 10$$

$$x_2 = x_2'' - x_2' \quad \dots\dots\dots\dots\dots\dots\dots\dots\dots\dots\dots\dots\dots\dots\dots\dots\dots\dots\dots\dots\dots\dots\dots 11$$

(See fig. 3)

Procedure and Analysis

A) Measurement of densities of irregular uniform solid objects.

i)   Turn on digital scale, set to grams, and zero the scale.
ii) Referring to the density measurement figure, a variety of unknown samples that have numbers written on them are first "weighed" to determine their masses. The numbers and masses are entered in the first two columns of Table 1. Note that the samples must be dry, i.e. free of attached water.
iii) A beaker about half-filled with water is placed on the scale and its mass m_1 determined. Write this mass in column 3.
iv) With the mass supported from above, submerge Mass 1 in the water without it touching the bottom or sides (see figure). Measure this new mass, m_2, and write its value in column 4.
v)   In column 5, calculate the object's volume using Eqns. 1 and 3.
vi) In column 6, calculate the object's density using Eqn. 2.
vii) Repeat these procedure steps for all the other samples. Note that the mass of the beaker with water must be measured each time since there is a small loss of water with the retrieval of each sample.
viii) Refer to the density table to determine the probable composition of each sample and enter your choice in the last column.

B) Comparison of the measured mass of a wood block to the mass of displaced water.

i)   "Weigh" the small wood block and record this value in the space provided below Table 1.
ii) Fill a one-liter glass beaker with about 700cc of water. Record the water volume as V_1 using the graduated scale on the side of the beaker.
iii) Place the wood block in the beaker so it floats freely. Record the new volume V_2 from the elevated water level.
iv) The difference in these two values is the volume of water that was displaced by the floating block of wood. Calculate the mass of the block using Eqn. 4.

C) Determination of the mechanical advantage of a hydraulic jack.

i)   Become familiar with the hydraulic house jack. Close the valve and pump up the piston so it becomes exposed a little. Measure the diameters of both pistons using a vernier caliper. Enter these values in the spaces provided below Table 1.
ii) Calculate the hydraulic mechanical advantage using Eqn.5 and write the result in blank provided.
iii) Measure the two lever arms and enter values in space provided. For the smaller L_1, use the vernier caliper to measure between centers of the pivot pins.
iv) Calculate the mechanical advantage of the pumping arm using Eqn.6 and write value in space provided.
v)   Calculate the total mechanical advantage using Eqn.7.
vi) Calculate what force one would have to apply to the pumping arm to lift the full weight of 24,000 pounds claimed by the manufacturer.

D) *Comparison of the velocity of a water stream calculated by Bernoulli's equation with that calculated from projectile motion.*

i)   Review the setup depicted in the final figure. The side of the can should allow one to drop a plumb line and determine x_2' on the meter stick. Record this value in the space provided.

ii)   Measure the heights y_0 and y_1 and record these values.

iii)   Measure distance, d, from the lip to the water level indicator and record this value.

iv)   Calculate $y_1 = y_0 - d$ and record value.

v)   With the hole taped shut, fill the can to the water level indicator.

vi)   Remove the tape and measure the position x_2"(at table level). Maintain the water level by adding water during this measurement. Record this x_2" value.

vii)   Calculate x_2 using Eqn.11.

viii)   Calculate the velocity two ways, Eqns.9 and 10 and compare the results.

_____   _____
        Your Name   Partner's Name

Table 1: *Measured densities of several unknown uniform solid samples.*

Object #	m (g)	m_1 (g)	m_2 (g)	V (cm³)	ρ (g/cm³)	Probable composition

Floating wood block

Measured mass of the block of wood _____

Water volume $V_1 =$ _____, $V_2 =$ _____

Calculate the mass of the block from the displaced water (show details below):

Mechanical Advantage of a house jack:

Piston diameter measurements: $d_1 =$ _____, $d_2 =$ _____

Lever arm measurements: $L_1 =$ _____, $L_2 =$ _____

Calculation of mechanical advantages (show calculation details):

   $MA_{hydr.} =$ $MA_{arm} =$ $MA_{total} =$

Calculate the force to lift 24,000 pounds. Leave answer in pounds.

Velocity of water stream calculated with Bernoulli's equation and from projectile motion.

$y_0 =$ _____ , $y_1 =$ _____ , $d =$ _____

Calculate $y_2 =$ _____

$x_2' =$ _____ , $x_2'' =$ _____

Calculate $x_2 =$ _____

Calculation of stream's velocity from Bernoulli's equation (show details below):

Calculation of stream's velocity from projectile motion (show details below):

Instructor's Signature

The Simple Pendulum   7

The effect of length, mass and amplitude on the period of a simple pendulum will be examined.

Introduction

A. Oscillations and Simple Harmonic Motion:

If a body is displaced from a position of equilibrium and experiences a force whose direction is opposite to that of its displacement, then the force will act to return the body to its equilibrium position and cause it to oscillate about that position. We can define two properties of oscillatory motion - namely, the **amplitude**, which is the largest displacement the body has from its equilibrium position while oscillating and the **period**, which is the time it takes for the body to go through one complete cycle of oscillation. In the special case where the magnitude of the restoring force () is also proportional to its displacement () from the equilibrium position, the motion of the body is called **simple harmonic motion** (SHM). The condition for simple harmonic oscillatory motion can therefore be expressed as :

$$\vec{F} \propto -\vec{s}$$

where the minus sign denotes that the force vector is oppositely directed to the displacement vector. If we introduce a proportionality constant, k, this expression can be written in the form :

$$\vec{F} = -k\vec{s} \quad \dots\dots\dots\dots\dots\dots\dots\dots\dots\dots\dots\dots\dots\dots\dots 1)$$

In terms of the acceleration, $\vec{a}$, we may write,

$$ma = -ks, \quad \text{or} \quad a + \left(\frac{k}{m}\right)s = 0 \quad \dots\dots\dots\dots\dots\dots\dots\dots\dots 2)$$

Equation 2) is the equation of motion for SHM. A solution has the form:

$$s = A\cos(\omega t)$$

where

$$\omega = \sqrt{\frac{k}{m}}$$

and A is the amplitude of the motion. The period, T, for SHM is then given by the expression:

$$T = \frac{2\pi}{\omega} = 2\pi\sqrt{\frac{m}{k}} \quad \dots\dots\dots\dots\dots\dots\dots\dots\dots\dots 3)$$

B. The Simple Pendulum (Small Amplitudes):

A simple pendulum consists of a small mass (the pendulum bob) which is held suspended from a string of negligible mass. When the pendulum is at rest it hangs vertically in its equilibrium position. When pulled to one side of this position and released it will oscillate about this equilibrium position under the influence of gravity. Only if the restoring force obeys eqn. 1) will this motion be simple harmonic. Referring to Fig. 1, this requires the restoring force to be proportional to the displacement s along the arc or alternatively, since $s = L\theta$, to the angular displacement θ.

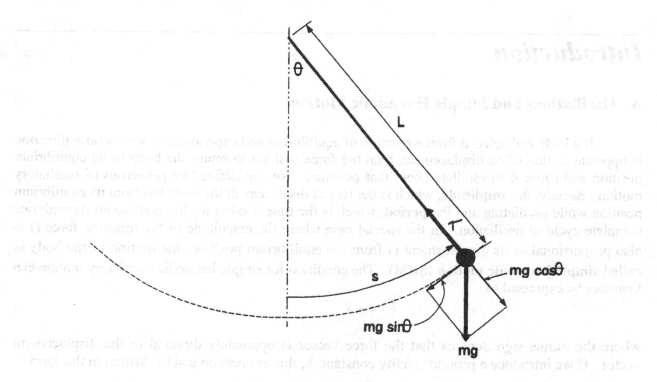

Figure 1. *Forces acting in a simple pendulum*

Two forces act on the mass when the pendulum is displaced through an angle θ from the vertical and these are the tension in the string τ, acting radially upward, and the weight acting vertically down. The weight can be resolved into a tangential component, $F_s = -mg \sin \theta$, in the opposite direction to the displacement and acting to restore the pendulum to its equilibrium position, and a radial component, $F_r = mg \cos \theta$. The restoring force is therefore:

$$F_s = -mg \sin\theta \quad\text{...4)}$$

Since the restoring force is proportional to $\sin\theta$ rather than θ, the motion of the simple pendulum is not exactly simple harmonic. However, if the angular amplitude is made sufficiently small ($\theta < 10°$, say) then:

$$\sin\theta \approx \theta \quad\text{...5)}$$

where θ is in radians.

The restoring force can now be closely approximated by:

$$F_s \approx -mg\theta$$

or

$$F_s \approx -\left(\frac{mg}{L}\right)s \quad \dots\dots\dots\dots\dots\dots\dots\dots\dots\dots\dots\dots\dots\dots 6)$$

Equation 6) shows that under the condition of small angular displacements the restoring force is approximately proportional to the displacement, s, and so the pendulum oscillates approximately with SHM. If we compare eqn. 6) with eqn. 1), the constant of the motion, k, is given by:

$$k = \frac{mg}{L}$$

Inserting this expression for k into eqn. 3), the period of a simple pendulum oscillating with small angular amplitude is:

$$T = 2\pi\sqrt{\frac{L}{g}} \quad \dots\dots\dots\dots\dots\dots\dots\dots\dots\dots\dots\dots\dots\dots\dots\dots\dots\dots\dots\dots 7)$$

The period of a simple pendulum oscillating with small amplitude therefore depends on its length and the acceleration due to gravity but is apparently independent of the amplitude of oscillation. Equation 7) also suggests a simple method for determining g by measuring T and L.

C. The Simple Pendulum (Large Amplitudes):

If the pendulum swings with large angular amplitude then eqn. 5) is not valid and the restoring force cannot be approximated by eqn. 6). We must now use the exact expression (eqn. 4) for the restoring force which is proportional to sin θ. Although the motion still has a characteristic period it is no longer nearly simple harmonic, and the period is also no longer independent of the amplitude.

Since sin θ is always less than θ in radians, the true restoring force is less than that predicted by eqn. 6). The acceleration of the pendulum at large angles is therefore smaller than in simple harmonic motion and consequently we may expect the period to be greater than that given by eqn. 7) for SHM. There exists no *exact* solution to the equation of motion which follows from eqn. 4) and the period for large amplitude oscillations can only be expressed as an infinite series of terms. Equation 8) shows the first few terms in the series representing the true period of a simple pendulum.

$$T(\theta) = T_0 + T_0\left[f(\theta) + g(\theta) + \dots\dots\right] \quad \dots\dots\dots\dots\dots\dots\dots\dots 8)$$

where

$$f(\theta) = \frac{1}{4}\sin^2\left(\frac{\theta}{2}\right) \quad \text{and} \quad g(\theta) = \frac{9}{64}\sin^4\left(\frac{\theta}{2}\right)$$

In this expression $T(\theta)$ is the true period of a pendulum having an angular amplitude θ and T_0 is the period in the limit of small angles given by eqn. 7). Equation 8) shows that the true period increases as the amplitude increases and, as noted before, is greater than the value of T_0.

The two terms in eqn. 8), $f(\theta)$ and $g(\theta)$, represent the first and second order corrections to the period. Contributions of higher order corrections in the expansion are not very significant. The relative importance of these terms can be examined by assuming initially just the first order correction and plotting a graph of $T(\theta)$ -vs- $(1/4)\sin^2(\theta/2)$. When the angular amplitudes θ are not too large, the second order term is unimportant and such a plot will yield a straight line with intercept T_0 and a slope of T_0 (eqn. 8). For very large amplitudes, the second term takes on greater importance and the first order approximation is no longer sufficiently accurate. This will show up on the graph as a systematic departure from a straight line at these large angles.

Procedure

All timing measurements will be carried out using a photogate incorporating an infra-red source and detector and interfaced to a computer for data acquisition. Two pendulums similar to Fig.1 have bobs with different masses and will be used to examine the effects of length and mass on the period. A third pendulum having a bifilar suspension will be used to study the effect of amplitude on period. In all cases, when the pendulum is hanging freely at rest the bob should be centered in the photogate and so that it blocks the IR beam.

Part A. Effect of Length:

i)   Measure and record the masses of both pendulum bobs. Select either one of the pendulums (which will be Pendulum A) and adjust its length to about 95 cm. Carefully measure this length (point of suspension to center-of-mass bob) and then align it so that its bob interrupts the photogate beam when hanging freely.

ii)   Double clicking on the *"Simple Pendulum"* icon brings up the *Home Page* for this experiment. Press the < CTRL R > keys to run the program and then enter your names here. Set the pendulum oscillating, and then proceed to *"Test Photogate"*. Follow the instructions to check that the photogate is operating properly.

iii)   Select "*Effect of Length* " and then *"Data Acquisition"* from the tab menu. Enter the length (in meters) and mass (in kg) of pendulum A in the control box and set the pendulum to oscillate with *small* (< 10°) amplitude.

iv)   Use the **BEGIN** and **END** buttons to collect data for about 15 oscillations. The computer will measure and display the periods for successive oscillations in the *"Trial Data"* box (see Fig. 2) together with the largest and smallest of the measured values, their mean value, and the standard deviation of the measurements about this mean. The standard deviation provides a measure of the experimental precision of the period measurement.

You will now be prompted whether or not you wish to permanently store this period in memory. Accept the measurement if the standard deviation is less than ±5 ms. If the standard deviation exceeds this, then the measurement can probably be improved and should be repeated.

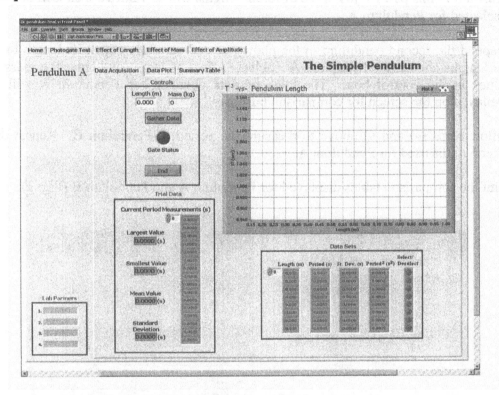

Figure 2. *Screen showing period measurements.*

v)   If you accept the measurement in step (iv), the data for that length will be saved in the "*Data Sets*" table and a data point plotted on the graph of T^2 –vs.- Length. You may print out this screen for your report as a record of the precision of your period measurements. You need not do this for every length; two cases from the experiment will be sufficient.

vi)   Reduce the length of the pendulum by about 10 cm and measure this new length.

vii) Enter the new length in the control box and repeat steps iv) and v). Repeat this for **at least** eight different lengths to cover the range 25 cm to 95 cm. Each time a measurement is accepted the "*Data Sets*" table and graph are updated.

viii) At the end of the measurements, select *Data Plot* from the menu and print a graph of T^2 –vs.- L. According to eqn. 7) this should be a straight line and the data are shown fitted with a "best fit" line calculated using the method of "linear regression" to determine its slope.

ix)   Select *Summary Table* to print a table of the results.

Part B. Effect of Mass:

The period of oscillation of the second pendulum (Pendulum B) which has a different mass will be measured in this part for just three different lengths whose values are chosen to correspond to any three selected for Pendulum A.

x)   Suspend the second pendulum in the photogate and carefully adjust its length to any one of the lengths chosen for Pendulum A. Select "*Effect of Mass*" and enter the mass and length values in the control box. The table of data obtained for Pendulum A will already be displayed on the screen for comparison purposes.

xi)   Follow steps iv) and v) above to measure the period of Pendulum B. Repeat this for two other lengths used for Pendulum A.

xii)   Print the comparison tables displayed for Pendulum A and Pendulum B (Fig. 3).

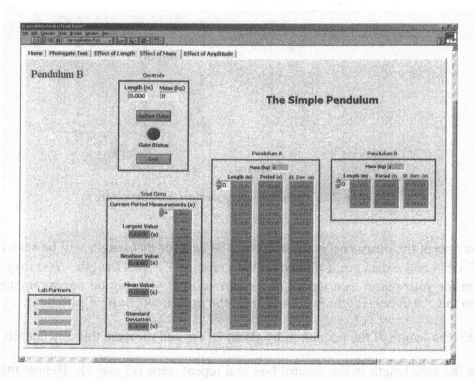

Figure 3. *Screen for mass-dependence study.*

Part C. Effect of Amplitude:

In this final part the effect of amplitude on the period of a simple pendulum will be examined. Since much larger angular amplitudes will be involved than in the previous studies, a pendulum having two 'angled' suspension cords will be used to give greater stability to the oscillations. The general arrangement is shown in Figure 4, in which the pendulum is seen to be suspended about a large protractor used to measure the angular amplitudes. Take measurements in 5° steps over the range 10° to 80°.

xiii)   When the pendulum is hanging at rest in its equilibrium position make any necessary adjustments to ensure it is aligned at the 0° position of the protractor and centered in the photogate.

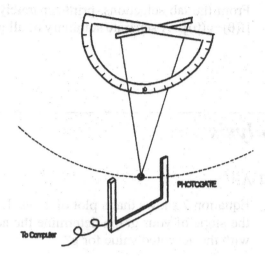

Figure 4. *Bifilar pendulum for amplitude study.*

xiv)   Select "*Effect of Amplitude*" then "*Data Sets*" and input the first angular amplitude, 10°, in the control box (see fig. 5).

xv)   Displace the pendulum through 10°, click on *Gather Data* button, and then release the pendulum carefully from rest. The period will be measured for one oscillation only. You will be asked to save or discard the measurement. If you accept the measurement, it will be stored in the *Data Sets* table and the amplitude displayed in the control box will automatically update by 5° to the next value (you may override this value if you wish).

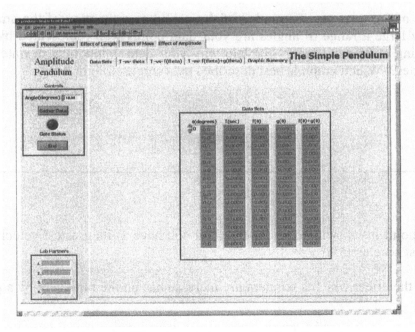

Figure 5. *Screen when measuring periods versus amplitude.*

xvi)   Repeat step xv) for the next amplitude value and continue in this manner out to 80°. In *"Data Sets"* obtain a printout of the table of period versus amplitude. This table also displays the values of the functions f(θ) and g(θ for each corresponding angle.

xvii) From the tab selections, print separately the three graphs T -vs.- θ, T -vs.- f(θ), and T -vs. - [f(θ)+g(θ)]. A separate summary of all graphs may also be printed.

Analysis

PART A:

i)   Equation 7 shows that a plot of T^2 vs. L should be a straight line with a slope of $4\pi^2/g$. From the slope of your graph determine the acceleration due to gravity. How well does this agree with the accepted value for g?

PART B:

ii)   From your data for the two dissimilar mass pendulums, construct a table to compare the periods where the lengths are the same. What do you conclude is the effect of pendulum mass on the period of a simple pendulum?

PART C:

iii) For each of the three graphs plotted of the period as a function of the amplitude of swing, over how large a range of angles are your data points well represented by a single straight line starting at 0° amplitude? Explain why your data points may deviate from this line at large angles? Which graph is best described by a single straight line?

Questions

1.   At what point in its swing does a pendulum bob have a) its greatest velocity, and b) its greatest acceleration?

2.   Describe the effect which a temperature increase has on the time kept by a pendulum clock.

3.   How would the period of a simple pendulum be effected if it were moved to an altitude of several hundred miles above the surface of the earth?

Transverse Mechanical Waves and Resonance

8

The relationship between wave velocity and tension in a string will be examined, together with the conditions necessary for two travelling waves to combine to produce resonance.

Introduction

A. Wave Velocity in a String Under Tension

Transverse waves which travel in a taut string are but one example of *mechanical waves*; i.e., waves which travel in elastic media. (Other common examples of mechanical waves are acoustic waves, which are longitudinal, and waves on a spring which may be either transverse or longitudinal.) If one end of a string which is held under tension is made to vibrate through one complete cycle, then this will cause a displacement pulse to travel down the length of the string, as shown in Fig. 1. The pulse is *transverse* because the displacement of the string is perpendicular to the direction of motion of the pulse. The velocity with which the pulse moves along the string depends on the tension F in the string according to the relation:

$$v = \sqrt{\frac{F}{\mu}}$$

1)

where μ represents the mass per unit length of the string, or its **linear density**.

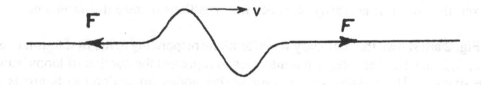

Figure 1. *A single wave pulse moving along a string under a tension F.*

We have here considered just one pulse travelling down the string. However, a train of such pulses may easily be generated to form a travelling wave by continually driving one end of the string back and forth at right angles to the length of the string. The frequency f of this travelling wave is equal to the frequency of the driving source, and the wavelength is the distance travelled by the wave in one complete cycle, which is related to the wave velocity and frequency through the equation:

$$v = f\lambda \qquad\qquad 2)$$

This leads to the relationship:

$$\lambda = \frac{1}{f}\sqrt{\frac{F}{\mu}} \qquad\qquad 3)$$

In general it is not a simple matter to make a direct measurement of the wavelength of a travelling wave. However, under appropriate conditions it is possible to set up so-called *stationary* (or *standing*) *waves* in the string which more readily enables a measurement of λ to be made.

B.   Standing Waves in a String

Consider a string which is fixed at both ends and held under tension. If one end is set into transverse vibration at some frequency f, a travelling wave moves along the string to the other end where it will be reflected. The resultant waveform established on the string will then comprise two travelling waves (the incident and the reflected waves) moving in opposite directions and having the same frequency and velocity. The nature of this composite wave will be determined according to the principle of superposition, and the actual configuration of the string can be very complex. However, under certain conditions the incident and reflected waves may combine in such a way as to produce a standing waveform, a condition known as *resonance*.

This resonant condition occurs when the length of string (L) between the fixed ends is just an integral multiple n of one half wavelength of the travelling waves,

$$\text{i.e.,} \qquad L = n\frac{\lambda}{2}, \qquad where\ n = 1, 2, 3,\ etc \qquad\qquad 4)$$

In this case the two travelling waves strongly reinforce each other at certain points along the string -the *antinodes* - where the string vibrates with maximum amplitude. At intermediate points - the *nodes* - the waves completely annul each other and the string has zero vibrational displacement. The string thus vibrates in a series of loops, with the nodes and antinodes remaining fixed in space. Since the ends are fixed they must of necessity be nodes i.e., positions of zero displacement.

In Fig. 2 are shown the stationary waveforms corresponding to the first four modes of vibration (i.e., n = 1, 2, 3 and 4). The integer n is also seen to represent the number of loops between the fixed ends of the string.† The distance between successive nodes (or antinodes) is just is just $\lambda/2$, thus providing a simple means for measuring directly the wavelength of the generated waves once the nodal positions are located in the stationary waveform.

---

† The different wavelengths obtained as n takes on increasing values are said to form a *harmonic series*. When n = 1, this corresponds to the *fundamental mode* of vibration, or *first harmonic*. Likewise, n = 2 corresponds to the *second harmonic*, or *first overtone*, n = 3 to the *third harmonic* or *second overtone*, and so on.

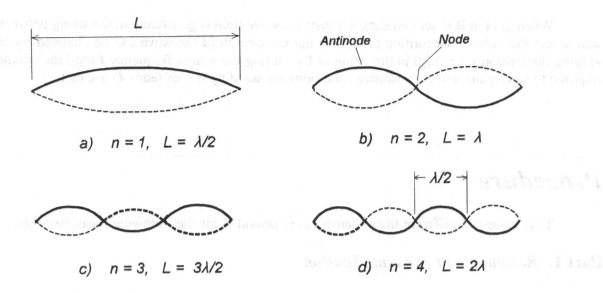

Figure 2: *Standing waves corresponding to the first four harmonics in a string under tension.*

The general arrangement for the experiment is shown in Fig. 3. The frequency source is an electrically-driven mechanical vibrator (VIB) with a pin (B) which can vibrate vertically. The pin is attached to the string near one end, and at the other end the string passes over a pulley (P) and has a weight of mass M hanging from it to provide tension (Mg) in the string. The frequency and amplitude of vibration generated by the source are adjustable and the frequency can be measured by means of a converted digital voltmeter.

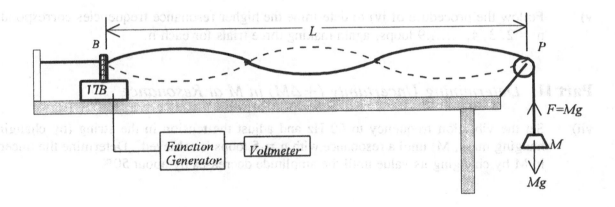

Figure 3: *Experimental arrangement for studying transverse standing waves on a string. The figure shows the string vibrating in its third harmonic resonance (n = 3 loops).*

When the pin B is set vibrating a transverse wave train is generated on the string between the source and the pulley. According to eqn. 3, the wavelength of the wave can be changed by either varying the tension F (= Mg) in the string or by varying the source frequency f until the conditions required to satisfy the various resonant conditions for standing waves (eqn. 4) are met.

Procedure

Two strings of different linear densities are provided for the following measurements.

Part I. *Resonance at constant Tension*

i)   A separate sample of the "heavy" string several meters long will be provided. Carefully measure its mass and its length. These measurements will be used to compute its linear density, μ.

ii)   Position the mechanical vibrator about 110 cm from the pulley and attach the shorter length of "heavy" string to its pin, B. Pass the other end of the string over the pulley and hang a mass of 250 gram from its end. Carefully measure (to the nearest millimeter) the length, L, of the string between the pin and the pulley.

iv)   Set the source vibrating and slowly increase the frequency until the string resonates with maximum amplitude in its fundamental mode, i.e., n = 1 loops on the string. (With this length and hanging weight, the fundamental frequency will be in the vicinity of 10 Hz.) Make three determinations of this fundamental frequency, by lowering the frequency and then returning to resonance for each measurement, and record your data in Table 1.

v)   Follow the procedure of iv) to determine the higher resonance frequencies corresponding to n = 2, 3, 4, ...9 loops, again making three trials for each n.

Part II. *Determining Uncertainty ($\pm \Delta M$) in M at Resonance*

vii)   Set the vibration frequency to 60 Hz and adjust the tension in the string (by changing the hanging mass, M) until a resonance with n = 5 loops is achieved. Determine the uncertainty in M by changing its value until the amplitude decreases by about 50%.

Part III. *Effect of String Linear Density*

viii)   Replace the "heavy" string with the "lighter" string provided. The linear density of this string is $\mu = 3.029 \times 10^{-4}$ kg/m. Repeat the procedure of Part I using the same 250 g mass as before. For this study a single trial for each resonance frequency will be sufficient. (Here the fundamental frequency is about 50 Hz.) Record your results in Table 2.

Analysis

i)   From your measurements in Part I, calculate the average frequency f for each value of n. Plot a graph of this frequency -vs.- n. Draw the best fit straight line through the data points and determine its slope.

ii)   According to eqns. 2) and 4), the slope of this graph is equal to v/2L, where v is the wave the wave velocity, v.

iii)   Calculate the linear density (mass per unit length) for the "heavy" string (step (i) in the Procedure)

iv)   Using eqn. 1), calculate the velocities of wave propagation on the strings in Parts I, II and III. What is the percentage difference between the wave velocity calculated for Part I and the corresponding value determined from the graph? In your report discuss their relative accuracies and the reasons for any discrepancies.

v)   Repeat i) and ii) for the light string.

Questions

1.   Verify that if the tension F is measured in newton and the linear density μ has units of kg/meter, then the quantity $\sqrt{F/\mu}$ has units of velocity in meter/sec.

3.   From equations 2) and 4), show that the slope of the f -vs.- n graph is equal to v/2L.

4.   Suppose the string in Part II is vibrating with two loops and at t = 0 the string is straight (displacement is zero everywhere). Sketch profile of the string at times t = 0, T/4, T/2, 3T/4, and T, where T is the period of vibration. Include arrows in your sketches to show the directions of motion of the string loops.

Appendix

Stationary waves are one of the most striking phenomena of wave propagation, providing an explanation even of the quantization of energy levels in atoms.

The concept of quantization of energy (energy having only certain allowed values rather than continuous values) was first applied by Max Planck to explain how the energy of the electromagnetic spectrum radiated by a body was distributed according to frequency, f. Niels Bohr then applied the concept to the hydrogen atom in order to explain its emission spectrum, showing that only certain electron orbits and energy values were allowed for the atom. The possible energy values are given by the formula:

$$E_n = -\frac{13.6}{n^2} \text{ electron-volts, where n = 1, 2, 3, ... etc.}$$

The integer n is called the *principal quantum number*.

In 1924 deBroglie proposed that particles can also exhibit wave properties and the wavelength of the deBroglie wave associated with a particle having momentum p was taken to be $\lambda = h/p$, where h is a constant known as **Planck's Constant**. When he applied his theory to the hydrogen atom he obtained agreement with Bohr's theory for the allowed electron orbits. In particular, he found that when the electron in its orbit was represented by its associated deBroglie wave, then only those orbits in which the circumference contains an integral number of wavelengths are allowed for the electron. Since the wavelengths were constrained to only certain allowed values so too were the energy values of the electron in the hydrogen atom.

The requirement of an integral number of wavelengths in the orbital circumference is precisely the condition necessary for setting up stationary waves in the orbit. The electron travels repeatedly around its closed orbit and when the condition for stationary waves is satisfied the wave associated with one particular electron traversal of the orbit combines **coherently** with the waves from previous traversals, giving rise to stationary nodes and antinodes. Thus, in this model, the discrete energy levels in the hydrogen atom can be understood in terms of the constraints required to set up stationary electron waves in the orbits. If the condition for stationary waves were not satisfied, then its waves would instead interfere **destructively** and its average wave intensity would vanish. Since the intensity of its associated wave must in some way represent its location, then a vanishing intensity is interpreted as meaning that an electron cannot exist in an orbit which does not satisfy the stationary wave condition. Fig. 4 illustrates the electron standing waves set up at a particular instant of time in the first three allowed Bohr orbits. The nodes and antinodes remain stationary in time although the signs and amplitudes of the oscillatory patterns will vary with time.

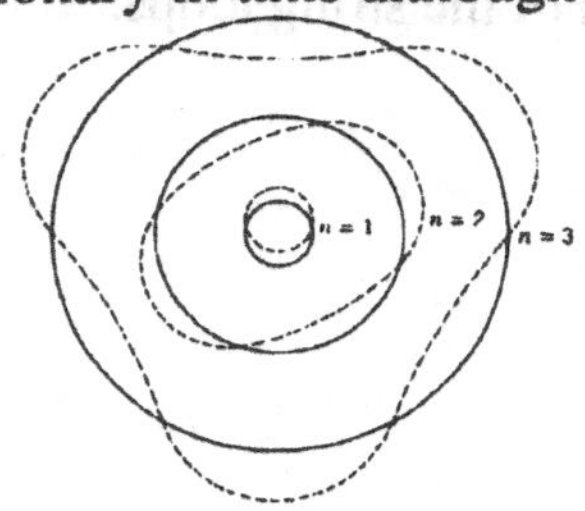

Figure 4. *Standing De Broglie waves set up in the first three Bohr orbits.*

Name: _____   Partner(s): _____

Part I. (Heavy String)

Mass of Heavy String,   m = _____ kg ;
Length of Heavy String,   l = _____ m;

∴ **String linear density**, μ (=m/l) = _____ kg/m

Hanging mass,   M = ___0.250___ kg;

∴ **String tension**,   F (= Mg) = _____ N

Length of resonating string (between source and pulley):

L = _____ ± _____ m

TABLE 1.

n	Frequency f_n (Hz)			Average frequency, f
	Trial 1	Trial 2	Trial 3	
1				
2				
3				
4				
5				
6				
7				
8				

Part II. (Heavy String)

Source frequency,   f = ___60___ Hz
Number of loops,   n = ___5___
Hanging mass,   M = _____ kg
Mass uncertainty,   ±ΔM = _____ kg
∴ **String tension**,   F = _____ ± __ N

Part III. (Light String)

(μ = _____ x 10^{-4} kg/m)

TABLE 2.

n	Frequency, f
1	
2	
3	
4	
5	
6	
7	
8	
9	

Heavy String

$v = \sqrt{F/\mu}$ = _____ m/s

v (from *slope*) = _____ m/s

Light String

$v = \sqrt{F/\mu}$ = _____ m/s

v (from *slope*) = _____ m/s;

Signature of Instructor: _____

Reflection, Refraction and Snell's Law

9

The laws of reflection and refraction will be studied and Snell's Law applied to determine refractive index.

Introduction

When a ray of light is incident at the boundary between two transparent media, part of the light is *reflected* at the boundary back into the first medium, and generally part of the light is transmitted into the second medium. The latter part is referred to as the *refracted* ray. We define the angles of incidence (θ_1), refraction (θ_2), and reflection (θ_3) as the angles which the respective rays make with the normal to the boundary, as shown in Fig. 1.

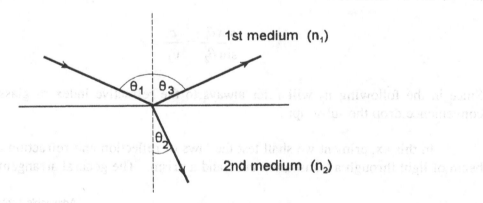

Figure 1: *Reflection and refraction at a boundary*

The law of reflection requires that the incidence and reflection angles be equal, i.e.

$$\theta_1 = \theta_3 \qquad\qquad 1)$$

If the first medium has an index of refraction n_1 and the second medium an index of refraction n_2, then according to Snell's law of refraction

$$n_1 \sin\theta_1 = n_2 \sin\theta_2 \qquad\qquad 2)$$

We see from this that

$$\text{if } n_1 < n_2, \text{ then } \theta_1 > \theta_2$$

and the refracted ray is bent **toward** the normal.

However,

$$\text{if } n_1 > n_2, \text{ then } \theta_1 < \theta_2$$

and the refracted ray is bent **away** from the normal.

The index of refraction of a medium is defined as the ratio of the velocity of light in vacuum (c) to the velocity in the medium (v), i.e.,

$$n = \frac{c}{v} \tag{3}$$

We may therefore write Snell's law in the form

$$\frac{\sin \theta_1}{\sin \theta_2} = \frac{n_2}{n_1} = \frac{v_1}{v_2}$$

in which v_1 and v_2 are the velocities of light in the first and second medium, respectively. In this experiment the first medium (n_1) will be air and the second (n_2) glass (or a plastic). Since at normal pressures the velocity of light in air is very nearly equal to that in vacuum, we may write $v_1 \approx c$ and $n_1 = 1.00$, in which case:

$$\frac{\sin \theta_1}{\sin \theta_2} = \frac{c}{v_2} = n \tag{4}$$

Since in the following n_2 will refer always to the refractive index of glass (plastic), we may for convenience drop the subscript 2.

In this experiment we shall test the laws of reflection and refraction by tracing the path of a beam of light through a transparent cube and a prism. The general arrangement is shown in Fig. 2.

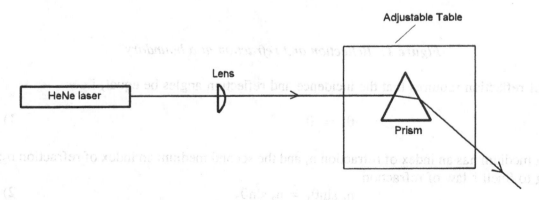

Figure 2: Experimental arrangement for ray tracing.

The light source used is a helium-neon (He-Ne) laser which emits a narrow, parallel beam of red light. For convenience in aligning the system the circular cross section of the beam is converted by means of a cylindrical plano-convex lens to a thin line. The lab-jack table and lens should be adjusted so as to produce a well defined narrow beam of light on the table surface.

Procedure

*WARNING: When working with a laser extreme caution must be observed. Above all, **never** look directly into the primary or any secondary reflected beams of the laser. The He-Ne laser used in these experiments produces about 0.5mW of radiant power over an area of about 0.5 mm², corresponding to an energy flux of 0.10W/cm². For comparison, the energy flux from the sun is about 0.14W/cm². Just as looking directly at the sun can cause eye damage, the laser beam may also be sufficiently intense to damage the retina.*

A. Cube

i)   Place the transparent cube and a sheet of white paper on the labjack top and obtain the ray formation depicted in Fig. 3(a). Draw in the outline of the cube and the path of rays a, b, c and d outside the cube. (If the cube has perfectly square sides, rays a and d will be parallel.) Remove the cube and complete the ray diagram. At the boundary points 1, 2, 3 and 4 in the ray diagram, draw normals to the cube surface and measure all corresponding angles of incidence, reflection and refraction. Enter their values in a table. Record also your estimated uncertainty in the angle measurements. *Note: the ray undergoes internal reflection without refraction (see Section B) at "3" and may not be observable from outside the cube. If so, work with points 1 and 2 only in the following.* From these data:

a)   Verify the law of reflection at the points 1, 2 (and 3, if possible).

b)   Apply Snell's law to calculate the index of refraction of the cube, n, and its estimated uncertainty, Δn, at each of the points 1, 2 (and 4, if possible).

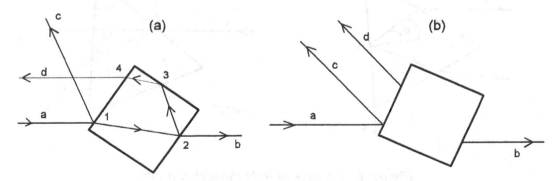

Figure 3: Passage of light through a cube.

ii)   Now change the orientation of the cube until the ray formation depicted in Fig. 3(b) is obtained. Follow the same procedure as before to obtain a complete ray diagram for this configuration and again calculate the refractive index and its measurement uncertainty at each point where refraction occurs. Combine all your values of n from (i) and (ii) and determine their average value (Table I) for this cube.

B. Prism

iii)   *Critical Angle*: Place the transparent prism on the labjack top and rotate it until the transmitted ray b just disappears (Fig. 4(a)). In this configuration the angle of refraction of the transmitted ray is 90°, i.e, the ray 'emerges' only by grazing along the prism surface. Under this condition the angle of incidence on that surface is called the *critical angle*, denoted by θ_c in the figure. Applying Snell's law to this boundary, we have

$$n \sin \theta_c = \sin 90° = 1$$

$$\therefore \qquad n = \frac{1}{\sin \theta_c} = \cos ec\, \theta_c \qquad\qquad 5)$$

Note that for incident angles greater than the critical angle θ_c, refraction can no longer occur and the light is *TOTALLY internally reflected*. This situation occurs only when a light ray passes into a medium of lower refractive index, as in the present case where the light emerges from the prism into air.

Draw the prism outline and all observable rays. (Be sure to note the location of boundary point 1.) Measure the critical angle and determine the refractive index from eqn. 5).

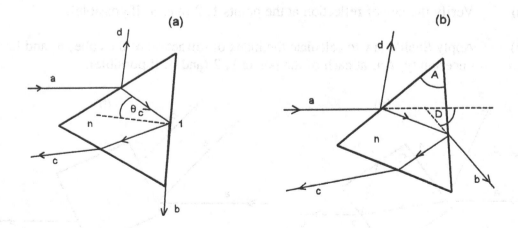

Figure 4: Passage of light through a prism.

iv)   *Minimum Angle of Deviation (MAD!)*: The angle of deviation is defined to be the angle which the emergent ray b makes with the direction of the incident ray a. This is the angle D shown in Fig. 4(b). Set the prism on the table and project the emergent ray b onto a nearby screen. If the prism is rotated slowly it is seen that, at one particular orientation of the prism with respect to the incident beam direction, the angle of deviation has a minimum value, i.e., $D = D_{min}$. With the prism set at this minimum angle of deviation trace its outline and all observed rays. Measure the angle D_{min}.

It can be shown that for this special orientation with the prism set at its minimum angle of deviation, the refractive index is given by the expression:

$$n = \frac{\sin\left(\dfrac{A + D_{min}}{2}\right)}{\sin\left(\dfrac{A}{2}\right)} \qquad\qquad 6)$$

where A is the apex angle of the prism (60° for the equilateral prism used in this experiment). Calculate n from your measured value of D_{min}. How well does it agree with the value found in step iii)?

Questions

1.   What are the velocities of light in the cube and in the prism? Using the table of refractive indices below (corresponding to red light), can you identify the materials used for the cube and prism from your measured average values? (This technique can be used to distinguish forgeries among gems.)

Quartz	1.46
Lucite	1.50
Zinc Crown	1.51
Polystyrene	1.55
Heavy Flint	1.64
Heaviest Flint	1.88

2.   A lamp is located 1m below the surface of a lake. Calculate the diameter of the area at the surface which is illuminated by the lamp, when viewed from above the surface. (The refractive index of water is 1.33.)

3.   When a ray of light is incident on a glass plate, the emergent ray is parallel to the incident ray but displaced from it. For a given angle of incidence in air, what are the two properties of the glass plate that determine the amount of lateral displacement?

Name: _____   Partner(s): _____

_____

TABLE I: Measurement Data for the Cube*

Boundary Point	$\theta_1 \pm \Delta\theta_1$ (in air)	$\theta_2 \pm \Delta\theta_2$ (in cube)	$\theta_3 \pm \Delta\theta_3$ (reflected ray)	$\sin\theta_1$	$\sin\theta_2$	$n \pm \Delta n$
Fig. 3(a)						
1						
2						
3						
4						
Fig. 3(b)						
1						
2						
3						
					Average n =	±

* θ_1, θ_2 and θ_3, are defined in fig. 1.

TABLE II: Measurement Data for the Prism

Prism Apex Angle, A =

Critical Angle (eqn. 5)	θ_c = $\pm\Delta\theta_c$ =	n = ±
Minimum Angle of Deviation (eqn. 6)	D_{min} = $\pm\Delta D_{min}$ =	n = ±
	Average n =	±

Signature of Instructor: _____

Converging Lenses: Aberration and Imaging

10

The properties of both thick and thin lenses will be studied and the role of Snell's Law in focusing examined.

Introduction

A. Thick Lenses and Aberration

Light rays passing through a converging lens will, according to Snell's law, be refracted by the lens to form a real image. If the light rays are initially parallel to one another and to the optic axis of the lens, then they will converge to one of the focal points of the lens. We can study the refracting properties of a lens using ray-tracing techniques. For this purpose a thick, *plano-convex* cylindrical lens will be used, having one flat surface and the second surface circularly shaped. (**Note:** Cylindrical lenses converge light in only one dimension whereas spherical lenses i.e., those with one or both surfaces spherically shaped, converge light in two dimensions.) Since the surfaces of the lens are of different shapes, the lens has different focal lengths on either side.

Although the light rays all converge, they do not all cross the optic axis at the same point. Parallel rays far from the axis are brought to a focus nearer to the lens than those close to the axis, which is a natural consequence of Snell's law of refraction. This imperfect focusing of the refracted rays, which leads to a blurring of any image formed by the lens, is referred to as *cylindrical aberration* (or *spherical aberration* in the case of spherical lenses). Aberration can be reduced, and the image therby sharpened, by introducing an aperture in front of the lens to allow only those rays which lie close to the optic axis to pass through the lens. Aberration is also a greater problem for thick lenses than for thin lenses.

B. Thin Lenses and Imaging

NOTE: See Appendix at the end of this experiment for a brief review of the properties of thin, positive lenses.

Given a lens of any shape and refractive index, the shape and location of the images it forms can always be determined by applying ray tracing techniques and Snell's law of refraction. However, for thin spherical lenses it is simpler to use the *Thin Lens Equation* to determine the location of an image. This equation has the form:

$$\frac{1}{d_o} + \frac{1}{d_i} = \frac{1}{f}$$ 1)

where f is the focal length of the lens, and d_o and d_i are the distances from the lens to the object and image, respectively.

If h_i and h_o are the heights of the image and object, then by definition the magnification of the object is h_i/h_o. Simple thin-lens ray tracing shows that the magnification can also be expressed in terms of the image and object distances and is given by the relation:

$$M\left(= \frac{h_i}{h_o}\right) = -\frac{d_i}{d_o}$$ 2)

(The negative sign follows from the sign convention for lenses.)

Procedure

Thick Cylindrical Lens

i)   Set up the optical bench arrangement as shown in Fig. 1. The Slit Plate allows seven rays from the light source through to the Ray Table. (The Ray Lens and Slit Plate may be mounted together on the same component holder.)

ii)   Without the cylindrical lens on the table, adjust the distance of the Ray Lens from the light source filament until the rays are observed to be parallel. Carefully align the central ray with the o-o axis of the Ray Table scale.

iii) Place the cylindrical lens on a sheet of paper on the table with its flat surface perpendicular to the incident rays. Adjust its position so that the central ray is undeflected by the lens and lies along its optic axis.

iv)   Carefully trace the outline of the lens and the paths of the seven rays on both sides of the lens. Do this for both lens orientations to determine both focal points (see insets in Fig. 1). Measure the two focal lengths of the lens.

v)   To examine the effect of aberration alone, set up the same arrangement as before with the flat surface of the cylindrical lens toward the light source. Trace the outline of the lens and the seven parallel incident rays. Identify each ray with a number. Now block all but the two outermost rays (use paper strips) and mark their point of intersection. Do this for other ray pairs and record the corresponding pair of ray numbers for each point.

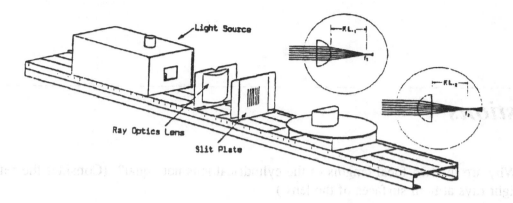

Figure 1: Optical bench arrangement for ray tracing.

Thin Spherical Lens

We shall next examine the predictions of eqns. 1) and 2). In particular, according to the lens equation a plot of $1/d_o$ -vs.- $1/d_i$ should yield a straight line having a slope of -1 and an intercept on each axis equal to $1/f$. Such a plot can, therefore, be used to determine the focal length of the lens.

vi)   Set up the arrangement shown in Fig. 2. The illuminated crossed arrow forms the object for the lens and is imaged on the viewing screen. Record the height of this arrow (h_o).

vii)   Keep the object fixed in position and move the lens until d_o = 100 mm. Now adjust the position of the screen until a well focused image is formed. Measure and record d_i and the height of the image (h_i) in Table I. Continue this for values of d_o up to 250 mm in step increments of 10 mm.

viii)   Return now to the region below do = 100 mm and find the smallest value of d_o for which a focused image can still be obtained.

ix)   Complete the calculations for the columns in Table I. How well do the values of magnification predicted by the relationship d_i/d_o compare with your directly measured values, h_i/h_o? According to the Lens Equation, the quantity $1/d_o + 1/d_i$ should be constant (and equal to $1/f$). How well do your results substantiate this? From the average value of this sum, determine the focal length of the lens.

x)   Plot a graph of $1/d_o$ -vs.- $1/d_i$. Determine the focal length of the lens from the average of the intercept values on the two axes. Is this value in agreement with that obtained in step ix)?

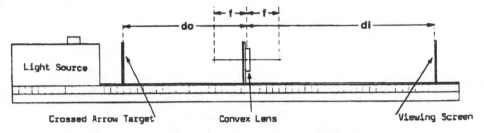

Figure 2: Arrangement for studying the thin lens equation.

Questions

1.   Why are the two focal lengths of the cylindrical lens not equal? (Consider the refraction of light rays at both surfaces of the lens.)

2.   How would you alter the shape of the lens to reduce the amount of cylindrical aberration?

3.   a) What was the smallest value of d_o for which you were still able to obtain a focused image on the screen? Use the Lens Equation to explain why.

       b) For any converging lens of focal length f, where would you place the object to obtain an image as far away as possible? How large would the image be?

4.   From your graph, determine the value of d_o which gives an image with a magnification of x1. Use the lens equation to show the relationship between this value and the focal length of the lens.

5.   Is it possible to obtain a non-inverted real image with a converging lens? A non-inverted virtual image? Explain.

Appendix

Positive (Converging) Lenses

Converging lenses have wide applications in many optical instruments, such as cameras, projectors, corrective glasses for vision. Figure A1 shows a set of light rays incident on a thin converging lens and all travelling parallel to the optical axis of the lens. The lens changes the direction of travel of the rays and they all pass through the same point, F, on the axis which is called the *focal point*, or *focus*, of the lens. The distance, f, between the focal point and the lens is the *focal length* of the lens.

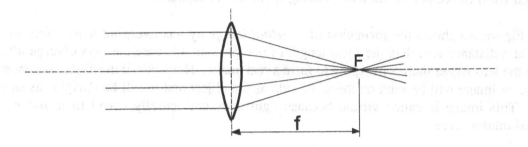

Fig. A1. *Focusing property of a thin converging lens.*

A converging lens can produce images as depicted in Fig. A2. An object O to the left of the lens is seen to produce an image I to the right of the lens. This image is inverted and *real* (that is, the light actually reaches the image which can be projected onto a screen and viewed without looking through the lens).

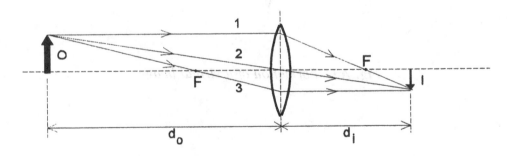

Fig. A2. *Formation of an image by a converging lens.*

Figure A2 also shows how to locate the image graphically: i) draw Ray 1 from some point on the object toward the lens and parallel to its optical axis. After passing through the lens this ray will be directed through the focal point. ii) draw Ray 2 from the same point toward the center of the lens. This ray will emerge from the lens undeviated in its direction of travel. The intersection of Rays 1 and

2 will be the image location of that point on the object. Ray 3 provides a further means for determining this location. iii) draw Ray 3 through the focal point of the lens on the same side as the object. On emerging from the lens it will travel parallel to its optical axis.

For a thin lens, the distances of the object, d_o, and the image, d_i, from the lens are related to its focal length through the following equation:

$$\frac{1}{d_o} + \frac{1}{d_i} = \frac{1}{f}$$

This equation can be derived by applying Snell's Law successively to the two surfaces of the lens. In a precise derivation the distances d_o, d_i and f are measured from special points associated with the lens called "*Principal Points*", whose positions depend on the lens thickness, the radii of curvature of its surfaces, and the refractive index of the lens material. However, for thin lenses the distances can be measured from the center of the lens, leading to the above equation.

Figure A3 shows the formation of a *virtual image* by a converging lens. Here the object is located at a distance less than the focal length of the lens. In this case the rays diverge after passing through the lens rather than converging to form a real image. However, if the object is viewed through the lens, an image will be seen on the same side as the object and it will be upright, as shown in the figure. This image is called virtual because light does not actually travel to it and it cannot be projected onto a screen.

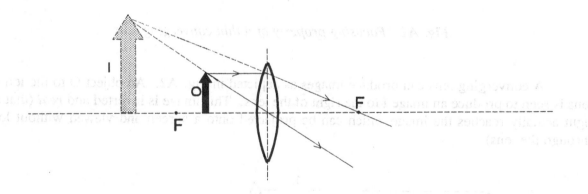

Fig. A3. Formation of a virtual image.

Name: _____   Partner(s): _____

_____

TABLE I: *Experimental data for Lens Equation*

d_o mm	d_i mm	h_i mm	$1/d_o$ mm^{-1}	$1/d_i$ mm^{-1}	$1/f =$ $1/d_o + 1/d_i$ mm^{-1}	Magnification	
						$-h_i/h_o$	$-d_i/d_o$
100							
					Average $1/f =$ mm^{-1}: $f =$ mm		

Signature of Instructor: _____

Wave Interference and Diffraction

11

Wave interference and diffraction will be examined using microwave radiation. The radiation wavelength will also be determined from the measured radiation patterns .

Introduction

Whereas all electromagnetic radiation travels with the same speed in free space (2.998×10^8 m/sec), the spectrum of electromagnetic radiation contains a wide range of wavelengths. Among the known sources, radio waves have the longest wavelengths (up to 10^5 m) and gamma radiation, which is emitted from atomic nuclei, contains the shortest known wavelengths (as small as 10^{-15} m). By comparison, visible light has wavelengths ranging from about 4×10^{-7} m (violet) to 7×10^{-7} m (red). Microwave radiation is the portion of the electromagnetic spectrum with wavelengths of the order of a few centimeters.

One of the earliest experiments demonstrating the wave nature of light was performed by Thomas Young in 1801. In this landmark experiment, light was allowed to fall on to two close-lying slits and the resulting illumination was observed on a screen. The pattern of illumination formed a series of bright and dark fringes which Young interpreted as due to wave interference. As a demonstration of this general property for all electromagnetic waves, we shall examine the Young double-slit experiment using microwave radiation.

A. Double-Slit Interference

Suppose a metal plate with two thin slits is placed perpendicular to the microwave beam, as shown in Fig. 1. Each slit will act as a new source of microwave radiation (Huygens' Principle) and the microwaves will radiate out at all angles into the region beyond the plate. This ability to penetrate into the geometrical shadow region is a property of all waves and is referred to as *diffraction*.

Since the two sets of waves radiating out from the two slits overlap in the region beyond the slits, they will interfere with one another and the intensity of radiation at any point in this region will be determined by the relative phase of the amplitudes of the two waves from the slits. Wherever the two wave amplitudes are exactly in phase they will reinforce each other (constructive interference) and produce a maximum intensity of radiation. Where the two waves are exactly out of phase, amplitude cancellation occurs (destructive interference) leading to a minimum intensity of radiation.

The relative phase of the two waves arriving at the receiver from the two slits is determined by the difference in their pathlengths. Constructive interference occurs if this path difference is a whole number (n) of wavelengths (i.e., BR - AR = $n\lambda$ in Fig. 1); destructive interference occurs whenever the difference is an odd number of half-wavelengths (BR - AR = $[n - \frac{1}{2}]\lambda$).

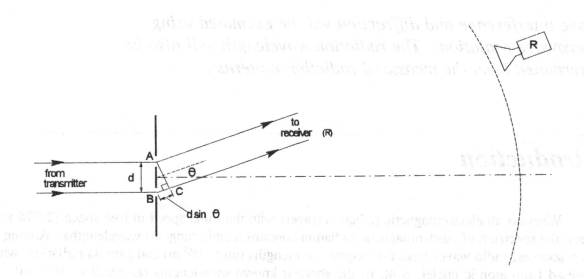

Figure 1: Double-Slit Interference.

Referring again to Fig. 1, if the distance from the two slits to the receiver is large compared with the separation d between the slits, then radiation from the two slits follow nearly parallel paths to the receiver and the path difference BR - AR = BC. If the receiver is positioned at an angle θ to the normal at the midpoint of the slits, the path difference BC between these nearly parallel paths is just d sin θ. In terms of this angle θ, the conditions for constructive and destructive interference (or maximum and minimum detected intensity, respectively) on either side of the principle maximum are then:

Constructive Interference: $d \sin \theta = n\lambda$ . . . . 1a)

Destructive Interference: $d \sin \theta = (n - \frac{1}{2})\lambda$ . . . . 1b)

where n is an integer (i.e., n = 1, 2, 3, . . .etc).

The intensity pattern observed in double-slit interference is shown in Fig. 2. (The central maximum at $0°$ corresponds to n = 0). Successive side maxima and minima correspond to increasing values of the integer n. The intensity pattern for double-slit interference shown in Fig. 2 assumes the width of each slit to be small compared to the wavelength of the radiation illuminating them. If this is not the case, the intensity pattern of Fig. 2 is modulated such that the maxima on either side of the central maximum decrease in intensity as n increases. This modulation is caused by the diffraction of radiation through each slit (see Section C).

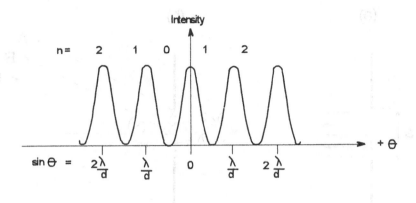

Figure 2:   *Intensity Pattern in Double-Slit Interference. (This intensity pattern assumes the width of each slit to be much smaller than the wave-length, λ, of the radiation.)*

B) Standing Waves

If a microwave transmitter is pointed toward a large metal plate, the plate acts as a mirror to the radiation and reflects the radiation back toward the transmitter. Since the reflected wave moves in the opposite direction to the transmitted wave and has the same wavelength, the resultant interference between the two creates a standing wave pattern between the transmitter and reflector (Fig. 3). Since the distance between adjacent nodes (or adjacent antinodes) is just λ/2 (see Experiment 10), the wavelength of the radiation can be readily determined.

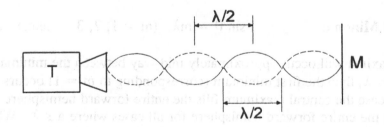

Figure 3: *Standing Microwaves*

C. Diffraction at a Single Slit

Figure 4 shows the radiation coming from a single slit whose width 'a' is assumed to be larger than λ/2. Each point on the wavefront incident on the slit can be considered, according to Huygens' principle, as a new source of radiation and the microwaves will diffract through all angles in the region beyond the slit. For diffraction at θ = 0° (fig. 3(a)), the path lengths of all rays from the slit are equal and the waves will remain in phase. The signal detected by the receiver at θ = 0°, therefore, corresponds to maximum intensity .

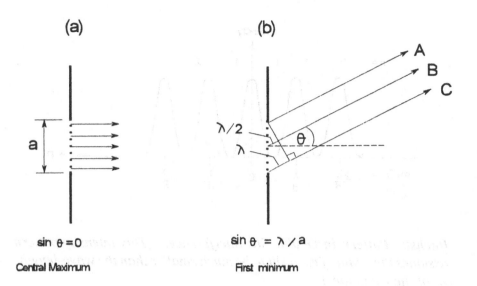

(a)

$\sin \theta = 0$

Central Maximum

(b)

$\sin \theta = \lambda / a$

First minimum

Figure 4: Diffraction from a single slit.

In Fig. 3(b), the observation angle θ is chosen so that the ray from the bottom of the slit (C) travels a distance λ further than the ray from the top of the slit (A). In this case, the wave along ray C is exactly out of phase with the wave along ray B since they differ in path length by $\lambda/2$. In fact, for every ray originating from the top half of the slit, there will be a corresponding ray from the lower half of the slit which is exactly out of phase with it, resulting in destructive interference. The radiation intensity detected by the receiver at this angle will, therefore, be zero. From the geometry of figure 3(b), this angle is given by the relation $\sin \theta = \lambda/a$. Additional minima may occur at larger angles, and the general relationship for the locations of intensity minima is:

Diffraction Minima: $a \sin \theta = m\lambda, \quad (m = 1, 2, 3, ...\text{etc.}) \quad \ldots \ldots \ldots \quad 2)$

Intensity maxima will occur approximately mid-way between the minima. From equation 2, it follows that if $a = \lambda$, then the first minimum (corresponding to m = 1) occurs when $\sin \theta = 1$, or $\theta = 90°$, in which case the central maximum fills the entire forward hemisphere. In fact, the central maximum occupies the entire forward hemisphere for all cases where $a \leq \lambda$. When $a > \lambda$, the first minimum occurs at $\theta < 90°$. The shape of the diffraction patterns for various values of a/λ is depicted in Fig. 5.

Figure 5:   *Intensity patterns due to diffraction from three single slits having different widths, 'a'.*

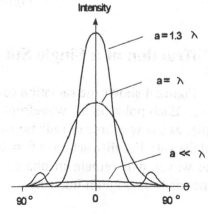

D. Diffraction from a Double Slit

As previously noted, the effect of diffraction at a double-slit is to modulate the interference pattern shown in Fig. 2 and repeated in Fig. 6(a) below. The diffraction pattern for each separate slit (Fig. 6(b)) effectively serves as an envelope about the double-slit interference pattern. The intensity pattern resulting from the combined effect of the two depends on the values of 'd' and 'a' relative to the wavelength, λ, but will generally have the appearance shown in Fig. 6(c).

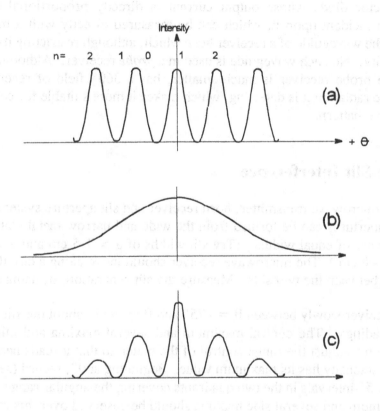

Figure 6: *The double-slit interference pattern (a) is modulated by the single slit diffraction pattern (as in (b) for the case a < λ). The combination of these two effects produces the intensity pattern depicted in (c).*

Procedure

The microwave transmitter employs a solid-state Gunn diode. The output radiation from this is linearly polarized and a waveguide horn attached to the transmitter gives rise to a directional beam of microwave radiation centered along the axis of the horn. The microwave *horn* receiver incorporates a semiconductor diode whose output current is directly proportional to the intensity of microwave radiation incident upon it, which can be measured directly with a microammeter. The diode is mounted in the waveguide of a receiver horn which, although restricting its angle of reception, increases its sensitivity. No such waveguide is used in a *probe* receiver. Although less sensitive than a horn receiver, the probe receiver is much smaller, has a 360° field of reception, and does not seriously obstruct the radiation it is detecting, which makes it more suitable for certain measurements like the standing wave pattern.

Part A. Double-Slit Interference

i)   Arrange the microwave transmitter, horn receiver and slit aperture system as depicted in Fig. 1. The slit apertures can be formed from the wide and narrow metal plates provided. Make sure the slits are of equal widths. (Try slit widths of a = 1.5 cm and a slit separation in the range d = 7 - 8 cm.) The microwave receiver should move along a circular arc whose origin lies midway between the two slits. Measure the slit separation, d, using a vernier caliper.

ii)   Move the receiver slowly between θ = - 75° and θ = +75° about the slit system and observe the meter readings. The central maximum and several maxima and minima on either side should be seen. Adjust the range control of the meter so that it reads nearly full scale where the radiation intensity has its maximum value. Beginning at 0°, record (see Table I) the meter readings at 2.5° intervals in the two quadrants covering the angular range -75° to +75°. The central maximum and several side maxima should be observed over this range, and additional measurements should be made to locate their precise angular positions. (If the slit system or transmitter are not precisely positioned about 0° on the angular scale, the central maximum may not be precisely located at 0°.) Angular separations of the side maxima and minima should be measured from the central maximum.

iii)   Plot a graph of your intensity readings as a function of the angle; note the change in amplitude of successive maxima. Each side maximum *and* minimum in the interference pattern will provide a value for the wavelength of the radiation by applying the relationship (equations 1) -

$$\lambda = (d \sin \theta)/n \qquad \text{for intensity maxima}$$
$$\lambda = (d \sin \theta)/(n - \tfrac{1}{2}) \qquad \text{for intensity minima,} \qquad n = 1, 2, 3, \ldots \text{ etc.}$$

Calculate the wavelength for each maximum and minimum observed.

iv)   Investigate the effect of increasing the slit separation, d.

Part B. Standing Waves

v)   With the microwave transmitter and a large metal reflecting plate separated by about 1-meter, use the probe receiver to locate a node at approximately 30-cm from the transmitter and record this initial position (x_i,-see Table II). Now move the probe through 10 succesive nodes and record its final position (x_f). Repeat this measurement for at least five determinations of the distance between ten nodes. Use different initial positions of the probe in these measurements.

From your table of data calculate the average distance, s, moved by the probe. Calculate the wavelength of the microwave radiation from these measurements.

Part C. Single-Slit Diffraction:

vi)   Construct a single slit arrangement centered at $0°$ and set its width to a = 1.5 cm as before. Adjust the range control of the meter so that it again reads nearly full scale at $0°$ and examine the single slit diffraction pattern out to $90°$. (If necessary, use the range control to to adjust the meter sensitivity at larger angles. Be sure to multiply your recorded entries by the appropriate scale factor indicated on the meter.)

vii)   Now set the slit width to a = λ. Using the horn receiver, examine the diffraction pattern once more in the region $0°$ to $90°$ and note any differences from your previous observations.

viii)   Set the slit width to 7 cm. Record the meter readings over the angular range $0° - 90°$. From your recorded data, plot a graph of the radiation intensity versus angle. Do the number of observed minima agree with the expected number for this ratio of a/λ?

Part D. Polarization

The microwave radiation from the transmitter is *linearly polarized*. For a Gunn diode transmitter, for example, the radiation propagates through space with its electric field vector aligned with the axis of the diode. If this axis is vertical, the transmitted wave is said to be *vertically polarized*. If the axis of the detector diode were at an angle to the direction of the electric field in the incident wave, it will only detect the component of the electric field vector which is aligned along its axis.

ix)   Arrange the transmitter and horn receiver so that they are directly facing each other at a separation of about 0.7m, with the receiver diode aligned with the vertical polarization of the incident beam. Adjust the receiver controls for nearly full-scale meter reading.

x)   Slowly rotate the receiver through an angle of 360° about the axis of the horn and note the meter readings. At what angles does the meter record minimum and maximum intensities of radiation?

xi)   Examine the effects which a microwave radiation polarizer (a metal plate with multiple parallel, narrow slits) has on the detected radiation intensity when placed at different angles between the transmitter and receiver.

Questions

1.   What frequency microwave radiation was used in this experiment?

2.   Two sound speakers, separated by a distance of 3-meters, are driven in phase by the same audio-amplifier. A listener sits directly in front of one speaker at a distance of 4-meters from it so that the listener and speakers form a right triangle. Find the three lowest frequencies which will not be heard by the listener. Where should the listener be positioned if all frequencies are to be heard? Use 340 m/sec for the velocity of sound. (HINT: The "dsinθ" approximation for determining the path difference from the two speakers is not valid in this situation (why?). The difference can be determined using simple geometry.)

3.   Explain why the image of a single narrow slit should appear sharper when illuminated with blue light than when illuminated with red light.

Name: _____   Partner(s): _____

_____

TABLE I: *Double-Slit Interference*

d = _____ cm

±θ°	I (μA) Positive Quadrant	I (μA) Negative Quadrant	±θ°	I (μA) Positive Quadrant	I (μA) Negative Quadrant	±θ°	I (μA) Positive Quadrant	I (μA) Negative Quadrant
0								
2.5			27.5			52.5		
5.0			30.0			55.0		
7.5			32.5			57.5		
10.0			35.0			60.0		
12.5			37.5			62.5		
15.0			40.0			65.0		
17.5			42.5			67.5		
20.0			45.0			70.0		
22.5			47.5			72.5		
25.0			50.0			75.0		

TABLE II: *Standing Waves*

x_i cm	x_f cm	$s = x_f - x_i$ cm
Average $\bar{s}$ (=5λ) =		cm

Signature of Instructor: _____

Wavelength of Light:
The Grating Spectroscope 12

A simple form of grating spectroscope will be constructed and used to measure the wavelengths of spectral lines emitted from mercury. The continuous spectrum emitted by a hot source (an incandescent lamp) will also be examined.

Introduction

A. Emission Spectra

When we observe a source of light directly by eye, we see only a single color which is a blend of all the various colors emitted by the source. A spectroscope is an instrument which enables the different colors to be separated (a process known as *dispersion*) to form a spectrum, so that each color may be studied individually. This separation may be achieved using either a prism or a diffraction grating. In this experiment we shall employ a diffraction grating. Since each color corresponds to a different wavelength of light, then we may describe the spectrum emitted by a light source according to the wavelengths of light which comprise it.

Emission spectra may be broadly classified into two types - *continuous spectra*, and *line* (or *characteristic*) *spectra*. When the spectrum of an incandescent solid, such as a lamp filament, is produced by a prism or grating, it is found to consist of a continuous band of colors containing all wavelengths, shading gradually from the violet (short wavelength) end of the spectrum to the red (long wavelength) end. Such a spectrum is referred to as a continuous spectrum and the relative intensities of different wavelength regions will depend on the temperature of the source. Thus, at low temperatures the spectrum is relatively intense in the red region, whereas at high temperatures it is more intense at the blue end. The spectrum is characteristic of 'white' light only if the relative intensities of the different wavelength regions correspond to a high temperature (i.e., white hot) light source, e.g., the sun.

On the other hand, the spectrum produced by rarified matter (for example, as produced when an electric discharge is passed through a gas such as in a fluorescent lamp) is found to consist only of a limited number of wavelengths. Thus, if light from a discharge tube is viewed through the entrance aperture of a spectroscope, the resulting spectrum will consist of a series of colored images of the aperture. Since the aperture is generally in the shape of a narrow vertical slit then these images appear as bright vertical lines, each corresponding to one of the component wavelengths, and the spectrum is referred to as a line spectrum.

The wavelengths and relative intensities of the lines in a line spectrum are characteristic of the particular atoms in the gas, and for this reason line spectra are frequently referred to as characteristic spectra. The interpretation of characteristic line spectra in terms of the structure of the atoms emitting the light is a major objective in atomic spectroscopy. Since different elements and compounds emit different line spectra, then this also provides a means for identifying unknown materials. This technique is the basis of spectrochemical analysis of materials. In this experiment the spectral lines of mercury will be measured and their wavelengths compared with accepted values (see Appendix A).

B. The Transmission Diffraction Grating

Though structurally very simple, the diffraction grating is one of the most important instruments devised for the study of spectra. A transmission grating consists of a large number of evenly spaced, fine slits very close together. The gratings employed in this experiment are either made using a holographic technique or are replicas of master gratings. These latter are made by means of a very accurate dividing engine which uses a diamond to cut very fine rulings on a plate of glass or speculum metal. The replicas are casts made from collodion films. The collodion is poured onto the master grating, and after drying it forms a tough film which retains the impressions of the rulings. This film is then stripped from the master grating and mounted upon optically flat glass plates.

The interference pattern expected from a double-slit arrangement was reviewed in Experiment 13, and the discussion presented there can be readily extended to a large number of slits, as found in a diffraction grating. As for a double-slit, the intensity pattern that results when monochromatic light of wavelength λ is incident on a grating consists of a series of interference maxima, or *fringes*. To understand this we may refer to Fig. 1.

Consider those rays diffracted through an angle θ from the incident light direction. These rays can be focused onto a screen at I by means of a converging lens. The relative phase angle between adjacent rays arriving at I will be the same as at the plane represented by the dashed line AB, and this is determined by the difference in path lengths traveled between the grating and AB [1]. If the separation between slits is d, then the path difference between adjacent slits is just dsin θ. If this path difference is equal to an integral number of wavelengths, then the rays all arrive at I in phase and therefore interfere constructively to produce a bright fringe of light (or image of the source) there. The condition for a bright fringe at I is, therefore,

$$d \sin \theta = n\lambda, \quad (n = 0, 1, 2, \ldots\ldots etc.) \; Constructive \; Interference \qquad 1)$$

which is the same relationship as obtained previously for just two slits separated by a distance d. Between the maxima, destructive interference occurs and there will be no illumination (dark fringes). It is obvious from symmetry that the same situation exists on both sides of O. Also, when n = 0, sinθ = 0 and there will always be a bright image at O (θ = 0°). Moving away from O, there will be

---

[1] Although the rays have different physical path lengths between AB and I, they nevertheless have the same optical path lengths, the higher refractive index of the lens material compensating for their different physical paths. Since rays haviong the same optical path lengths contain the same number of wavelengths, the presence of the lens introduces no additional phase difference at I.

a region of no illumination and then the first bright side-fringe (corresponding to n=1) occurs at a diffraction angle given by $d \sin\theta_1 = \lambda$. This is referred to as the *first-order spectrum*. Continuing away from O, the next bright fringe will occur for n = 2 (the *second-order spectrum*) at an angle θ_2 given by $d \sin\theta_2 = 2\lambda$, and so a pattern of bright and dark fringes are formed on either side of O.

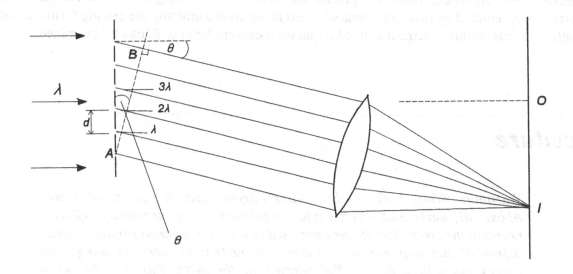

Figure 1: *Formation of the first-order (n=1) image by a diffraction grating.*

Note that the locations of the interference maxima do not depend on the total number of slits in the grating. However, a more detailed study shows that the intensities of the maxima increase and their widths decrease as the number of slits increases, thus producing much sharper and brighter fringes more suitable for spectroscopic studies.

If the light source is monochromatic (i.e., consists of only one wavelength, or color), then the image in each order consists simply of a single colored image of the source, and the angle θ is unique for each order. If, however, the source is heterochromatic (i.e., consists of several different wavelengths) then in each order there will be several different colored fringes, one for each wavelength. This can be seen from eqn. 1), since for a given order (or value of n) there will be a different value of θ for each of the various wavelengths. The component wavelengths in a light source can therefore be separated and individually studied. A helium-neon laser is an example of a monochromatic source, emitting light only at 6328 Å. A mercury-vapor lamp, on the other hand, is heterochromatic, emitting light at several different wavelengths [2].

---

[2] The wavelengths of light in the visible region may be expressed in meters, but this is not usual since it is so large a unit. More common units are the Angstrom unit, Å ($1\text{Å} = 10^{-10}$ m), the nanometer, nm ($1\text{nm} = 10^{-9}$ m), or the micron, μ ($1\mu = 10^{-6}$ m). For example, the wavelength of light emitted by a He-Ne laser (6.328×10^{-7} m) might be expressed as 6328Å, 632.8 nm, or 0.6328 μ.

There are three essential parts to this experiment. The first involves a measurement of d, the separation of adjacent slits in the diffraction grating. (The replica gratings are *nominally* rated at either 7500 lines/inch or 10,000 lines/inch, which are the line densities of the master gratings from which the replicas were prepared. However, during the drying and stripping process, a slight contraction of the casts usually increases the number of lines per inch, and for this reason it is necessary to calibrate each grating separately to determine the precise line density.) Knowing d, the wavelength of the characteristic lines emitted by mercury atoms will next be measured utilizing the grating formula, eqn. 1). Finally, the continuous spectrum emitted by an incandescent lamp will also be examined.

Procedure

*Warning: When working with a laser extreme caution must be observed. Above all, **never** look directly into the primary or any secondary reflected beams of the laser. The He-Ne laser used in these experiments produces about 0.5mW of radiant power over an area of about $0.5mm^2$, corresponding to an energy flux of 0.10 W/cm^2. For comparison, the energy flux from the sun is about 0.14 W/cm^2. Just as looking directly at the sun can cause eye damage, the laser beam may also be sufficiently intense to damage the retina.*

Measurement of the Grating Constant, d

A diffraction grating is a precision instrument and must be handled with great care. Never touch a grating surface and only handle it by the edges of the glass mount.

Determination of the grating constant, d, is made using light of known wavelength and employing the grating formula, eqn. 1). In the present case we shall use the monochromatic light emitted by a He-Ne laser, with $\lambda = 6328$Å. The general arrangement is shown in Fig. 2, in which the laser, grating G, and screen are all mounted on an optical bench AB.

i)   To ensure normal incidence of the laser beam on the grating, adjust the grating until the reflected component of the beam returns to the laser source aperture. Adjust the distance l between the grating and screen so that at least the first- and second- order images (n=1 and n=2) are observed on the screen. Record the values of l, y and n (see Fig. 2 and Table I) for the four images on either side of the central maximum at O [3].

---

[3] In determining l, note that with the carriage scales used in this experiment the actual grating position is displaced 1 cm from the indicated position of the grating carriage.

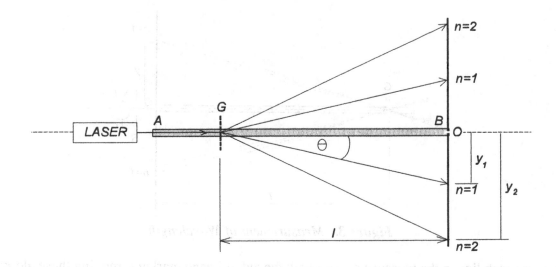

Figure 2: *Determination of Grating Constant, d.*

In determining y_1 (corresponding to the first-order image, n = 1) and y_2 (corresponding to the second-order image, n = 2), the positions of the images to the left and right of O should be noted which then yield the values $2y_1$ and $2y_2$. This avoids the need to determine the exact location of O on the screen.

ii)   Repeat this process for a larger distance l such that the first-order images occur near the ends of the screen.

iii)   For each set of measurements calculate the grating constant d (in cm.) using the grating formula, and compute the average value of the measurements, $\overline{d}$. What is the corresponding number of lines/inch for the grating? How does this compare with the given 'nominal' rating?

Mercury Spectrum

The experimental set-up is illustrated in Fig. 3. A 2-meter rule serves as a screen and is mounted close to a vertical slit S at one end of an optical bench, with their planes perpendicular to the bench. The full length of the slit should be just visible above the meter rule. Mount the grating G near the other end of the optical bench, with its plane also perpendicular to the bench, and measure its distance from the slit. (This simple arrangement illustrates the basic principles of a grating spectroscope.)

iv)   Set-up the mercury lamp L behind the slit and, with the eye close to the grating, view the images of the slit on either side of O. At least the first- and second-order spectra should be seen above the meter rule. Since the mercury spectrum is composed of many wavelengths, then in each order these various wavelengths will be diffracted through different angles and the image of the slit becomes a line spectrum composed of a series of bright, colored images.

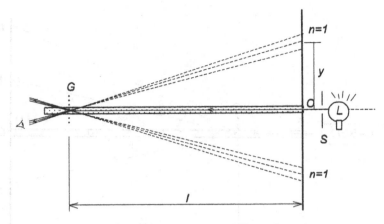

Figure 3: Measurement of Wavelength

Locate each line in the mercury spectra with the aid of image markers, moving these along the 2-meter rule until they appear to coincide with each corresponding pair of lines on either side of O. A parallax test will show that an image and its marker may not be precisely at the same distance from the eye. To minimize parallax errors, all measurements should be made by sighting through the same portion of the grating. Record the values of 2y for each spectral line on either side of O, in both the n = 1 and n = 2 orders. Convert these values to corresponding angles (see Table II).

v) The two yellow lines are very close and might only be seen separated in the n=2 or higher order spectra. Position the image marker in the center of the doublet to measure their average wavelength. In the n=2 order spectrum, estimate their separation, Δy, and use this to calculate their difference in wavelength. (See eqn. B1 in Appendix B for this calculation.) Repeat this also for the n=3 spectrum. Compare these values with the accepted value of 21Å.

Observe the higher order spectra. What differences in the spectra do you see as you move out to higher orders? Which order spectra (if any) overlap?

vi) Using the grating formula and your value for $\overline{d}$, calculate the wavelength of each spectral line in both the first- and second-order spectra. These wavelengths are denoted by λ_1 and λ_2 in Table II. From their values compute the average wavelength for each line.

vii) Construct a table comparing your measured wavelengths with accepted values, which are listed in the Appendix. Do they agree within the limits of the experimental uncertainty?

The Continuous Spectrum

viii) Now replace the Hg lamp with the incandescent filament lamp. This can be operated at different filament temperatures by adjusting the operating voltage. Record your observations concerning the effect of temperature on the continuous spectrum. Estimate also the boundary wavelengths of each colored region of the spectrum when the filament temperature is a maximum (λ_R, λ_G, λ_B...etc.), showing these in a diagram such as Fig. 4. (Use a linear wavelength scale for this purpose.)

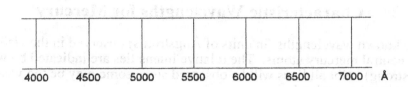

Figure 4: *Wavelength Limits in a Continuous Spectrum*

Questions

1. Using your measured value for the grating constant, $\overline{d}$, calculate the angular spread of the visible spectrum (4000-7000 Å) in the first-order and second-order spectra. What advantages might there be in taking spectral measurements in the second-order rather than in the first?

2. Using again your measured grating constant, in how many orders can the full range of the visible spectrum be produced?

3. A grating is illuminated with light from a He-Ne laser as well as with light having an unknown wavelength. It is observed that the fourth-order image for the laser light coincides in position with the fifth-order image of the unknown wavelength. What is the unknown wavelength?

APPENDIX A

Characteristic Wavelengths for Mercury

The following are known wavelengths (in units of Ångstroms) observed in the visible region of the line spectrum for neutral mercury atoms. The relative intensities are indicated by w (weak), m (medium) and s (strong). Not all lines will be observed since some may be too weak and others so closely spaced as to not be resolved.

Color	Violet	Blue	Green	Yellow	Orange	Red
Wavelength – (Strength)	4047 (s) 4078 (m)	4339 (w) 4348 (w) 4358 (s)	4916 (m) 4960 (w) 5461 (s) 5676 (w)	5770 (s) 5791 (s)	6073 (w) 6123 (w) 6234 (w)	6907 (s)

APPENDIX B

Wavelength Difference for the Hg Yellow Doublet

Suppose the center of the yellow doublet in the nth-order spectrum occurs a distance y from the optical axis and the two lines are separated by Δy due to their wavelength difference $\Delta\lambda$. At the grating, y corresponds to an angle θ and Δy to an angular separation $\Delta\theta$. The grating formula gives us $n\lambda = d\sin\theta$, where d is the slit separation in the grating and λ the average wavelength of the doublet. Upon differentiating we have:

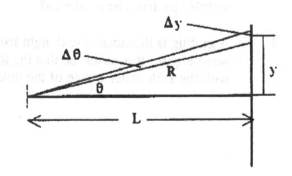

$$d\lambda = \frac{d}{n}\cos\theta \; d\theta$$

If we substitute the small incremental changes $\Delta\lambda$ and $\Delta\theta$ for the differential terms, and noting that

$$\Delta y = \frac{R\,\Delta\theta}{\cos\theta} \;\;,\;\; \text{or}\;\; \Delta\theta = \frac{\cos\theta\,\Delta y}{R}\;\;,\;\; \cos\theta = L/R \;\; \text{and}\;\; R = \sqrt{L^2 + y^2}\;,\;\; \text{we have:}$$

$$\Delta\lambda = \left(\frac{d}{n}\right)\left(\frac{L^2}{\left(L^2 + y^2\right)^{3/2}}\right)\Delta y \qquad\qquad \text{B1)}$$

Name: _____   Partner(s): _____

_____

TABLE I. *Determination of Grating Constant*

λ (He-Ne laser) = 6328 Å

ℓ (cm)	n = 1				n = 2				d = nλ/sinθ	
	$2y_1$ (cm)	$\tan\theta_1 = \dfrac{y_1}{\ell}$	θ_1°		$2y_2$ (cm)	$\tan\theta_2 = \dfrac{y_2}{\ell}$	θ_2°		n = 1	n = 2
									$\lambda/\sin\theta_1$	$2\lambda/\sin\theta_2$
$\ell_1 =$										
$\ell_2 =$										

$\overline{d} =$ _____ cm

TABLE II. *Calculated Wavelengths for Mercury Lines Spectra*

ℓ = _____ cm

Line Color	n = 1			n = 2			$\lambda = \dfrac{\overline{d}\sin\theta_n}{n}$	
	$2y_1$ (cm)	$\tan\theta_1 = \dfrac{y_1}{\ell}$	θ_1°	$2y_2$ (cm)	$\tan\theta_2 = \dfrac{y_2}{\ell}$	θ_2°	n = 1	n = 2
							$\lambda_1 = \overline{d}\sin\theta_1$	$\lambda_2 = \dfrac{\overline{d}\sin\theta_2}{2}$

Signature of Instructor: _____

Latent Heat of Fusion

*By measuring the change in temperature when ice is melted in a
quantity of water, the latent heat of fusion of water will be
determined.*

Introduction

When heat is added to a body under constant pressure, this usually results in an increase in the temperature of the body. Sometimes, however, a body may absorb heat without any change in temperature. This happens when the physical condition, or ***phase***, of the material is changing from one form to another, e.g., solid $\leftrightarrow$ liquid, or liquid $\leftrightarrow$ gas.

If a substance changes phase from the solid to the liquid state, the molecules, which were initially held close together in the solid because of attractive force, are moved farther apart. This requires that work be done against the attractive forces and this is provided by adding energy to the substance in the form of heat. While the phase change is taking place, the average kinetic energy of the molecules remains unchanged and, therefore, the temperature of the substance remains constant. If heat is still added after the phase change is completed (i.e., after the substance is entirely liquid) then the energy is now used to increase the kinetic energy of the molecules and so the temperature begins to rise. A further increase in the separation of the molecules occurs when the phase changes from liquid to gas and during this change the temperature again remains constant until all the liquid is converted to the gaseous state. Phase changes occur only at particular temperatures. For example, pure water at atmospheric pressure changes from solid to liquid at $0°C$ (ice point) and from liquid to gas at $100°C$ (steam point).

For a pure substance, a definite quantity of heat is needed to change its phase, the amount being proportional to its mass, i.e.:

$$Q = mL$$

where L is a constant characteristic of the particular substance and kind of phase change involved (usually denoted by a subscript). If the phase change is solid $\rightarrow$ liquid, L_f is called the latent heat of fusion of the substance. If the change is liquid $\rightarrow$ gas, L_v is called the latent heat of vaporization. The same quantities of heat must also be *extracted* from a substance if the phase change is reversed (i.e., gas $\rightarrow$ liquid, or liquid $\rightarrow$ solid).

In the present experiment, the latent heat of fusion of water will be determined by adding ice to a quantity of water in a calorimeter at initial temperature T_i, and measuring the resulting temperature change. If the calorimeter is well insulated so that no heat is exchanged with its environment, then we can equate the heat lost by the water and calorimeter to the heat gained by the ice. If the mass of the calorimeter is M_c, then the heat given up by the water and calorimeter after the ice is added is given by:

$$Heat\ Lost = M_w c_w (T_i - T_f) + M_c c_c (T_i - T_f) \quad \text{.............................} \quad 1)$$

where c_w is the specific heat of water, c_c is the specific heat of the calorimeter, and T_f is the final temperature of the system. If m_i is the mass of ice added to the water, the heat gained by the ice is:

$$Heat\ Gained = M_i L_f + M_i c_w (T_f - 0) \quad \text{.......................} \quad 2)$$

This quantity is seen to comprise two terms. The first term is the heat required to melt the ice to form water (still at $0\overset{\circ}{}C$), and the second represents the additional heat which raises the temperature of the melted ice from $0\overset{\circ}{}C$ to T_f. Assuming no heat is lost from the calorimeter, then:

$$M_i L_f + M_i c_w (T_f - 0) = M_w c_w (T_i - T_f) + M_c c_c (T_i - T_f)$$

or,
$$L_f = \frac{(M_w c_w + M_c c_c)(T_i - T_f) - M_i c_w T_f}{M_i} \text{cal.g}^{-1} \quad \text{.......................} \quad 3)$$

By measuring the masses and temperature changes involved, the latent heat of fusion of water can thus be determined.

Procedure

Probe Test

i).   A temperature probe interfaced to a computer will be used to monitor the water temperature. The probe should be connected to terminal A on the interface module, the module connected to the computer, and the probe resting on the bench at room temperature. The probe will first be tested for proper operation and then calibrated against a regular thermometer at three or more different temperatures before beginning the calorimeter readings.

ii).   On the desktop select the program "*Latent Heat*" which brings up the *Home* page for this experiment. Press the <CTRL R> keys and then enter your names. Tab next to "*Test Probe*" which will test whether the probe is functioning properly. At this stage, the computer simply reads and displays the probe voltage output (in mV). Press the **Begin** button to start the test. If the probe is in temperature equilibrium with the room, its voltage should be steady and lie in the range xxxx- yyyy mV. If this is not so, consult your instructor. Press **End** to finish the test.

Probe Calibration

iii). Tab next to "*Calibrate Probe*" (fig. 1) and press *Begin Calibration*. With the probe still at room temperature, press record when the voltage reads a steady value. A pop-up window now appears allowing the temperature to be entered from a thermometer alongside the probe. If you accept this reading, the program returns to the *Calibration* page and enters the data in a table and on a graph of Temperature –vs.- Voltage.

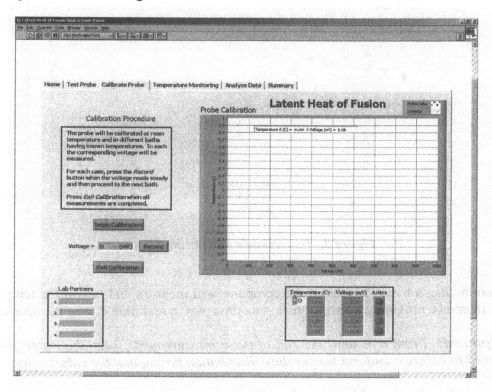

Figure 1. Probe Calibration screen

iv). Repeat step iii) for two or more lower temperatures (use a mixture of ice and water baths to obtain these temperatures), entering the corresponding temperatures when the voltage readings are stable. Be sure the baths are well stirred before you take their thermometer readings. The data are fitted with a straight line graph using linear regression and the calibration parameters are stored in memory to read the future temperatures directly with the probe. When finished calibrating, print the calibration screen and press the *End Calibration* button.

Temperature Monitoring

v). Tab to *Temperature Monitoring* (see fig.2). Enter as input data the specific heats of the calorimeter and water as well as the mass of the empty **inner** calorimeter cup (M_c). Fill the cup about two-thirds with water at room temperature. Reweigh and record the new mass (M_1) to determine the mass of water (M_w). Place the cup in the calorimeter, position the lid, and place the probe in the water.

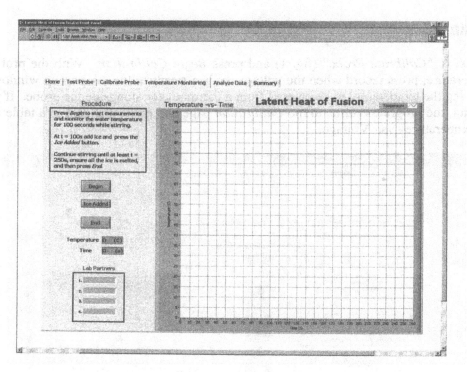

Figure 2. *Temperature Monitoring screen*

vi). When the *Begin* button is pressed the computer will measure and record the temperature at 1-sec. intervals, providing a temperature -vs.- time plot in real time during the measurements.

> *Important*: *From now until the end of these measurements, keep the water gently stirred to ensure a uniform temperature distribution throughout the calorimeter.*

vii). At t = 100s, take about 25g of ice from the ice/water bath, quickly dry it, and transfer it to the calorimeter. Press the *Ice Added* button. Since it is important that all the ice melts, be careful not to add so much that the temperature of the water is lowered too close to the ice point.

viii). Continue measurements until about t = 250s and then press *End* to finish. Print this screen to show the graph of temperature -vs.- time and then tab to *Analyze Data*.

ix). Remove the temperature probe carefully so as not to lose any water from the calorimeter. Weigh and enter as input the mass of the calorimeter cup and its contents (M_2). The difference between this and the previous mass (M_1) gives the mass of the added ice (M_i). The initial and final temperatures are displayed on this screen. Select *Analyze* to calculate the latent heat from these input and measured data and print this screen for your report.

x). Empty the calorimeter and repeat steps v) through ix) for two further measurements.

xi). By tabbing to *Summary*, all measurement results are tabulated and corresponding graphs plotted for inclusion in your report.

Analysis

i)   Calculate the average value of your latent heat from the three measurements. What is the percentage difference between this value and the accepted value? Can this be explained by your estimated measurement uncertainties?

ii)   Select one of the measurements from the Summary Table. Determine the masses of the water and ice used and calculate the latent heat using eqn. 3). Does this agree with the computer calculation shown in the Summary Table?

Questions

1.   Why was it necessary to dry the ice before transferring to the calorimeter? How might your results have been affected had you not dried it?

2.   The ice used in this experiment was obtained from a freezer at -15°C. It was assumed in your analysis, however, that the temperature of the ice when added to the calorimeter was precisely 0°C. What step was taken in the experiment to ensure that it was at 0°C?

3.   If the calorimeter did not provide good thermal insulation, how would the temperature of its contents have changed with time - a) during the period before the ice was added, and b) after the ice had fully melted? From inspection of your temperature -vs.- time graphs, what can you conclude about the effectiveness of the insulation?

Thermal Radiation: Stefan-Boltzmann's Law **14**

The effect of temperature on the rate at which energy is radiated by a hot body (Stefan-Boltzmann's law) will be investigated.

Introduction

A. Radiant Energy

The transfer of heat energy from one body to another occurs via three mechanisms: conduction, convection and radiation. Conduction requires direct contact between the two objects. Convection requires an intervening fluid which transfers heat energy by means of upward-moving currents in the fluid. In the case of radiation, heat is transferred directly by electromagnetic waves travelling at the speed of light, even through vacuum. Heat from the sun, for example, reaches us by means of radiation through the vacuum of outer space. The warmth we feel from a fire is also mostly in the form of radiant energy since most of the heated air rises by convection up the chimney and does not reach us.

All objects continually lose energy by radiation. The rate at which energy is radiated from a surface depends on the nature of the surface and on its temperature, with the rate of emission increasing with temperature. The radiation contains a mixture of wavelengths in the electromagnetic spectrum and this mixture also depends on the temperature. For example, a body at relatively low temperatures, say <300°C, will radiate energy almost entirely in the invisible infrared region of the spectrum. At about 800°C, the radiation will include wavelengths in the visible red as well as the infrared region, and the body will appear 'red hot'. An object at 3000°C, such as an incandescent lamp filament, contains radiation covering the entire visible region (red to violet) of the electromagnetic spectrum in addition to infrared radiation, and will appear 'white hot'.

The rate that energy is emitted by a body (its radiant power or intensity of radiation) increases very rapidly with the temperature of the body and is given by the Stefan-Bolzmann law of radiation. This states that the rate at which energy is radiated per unit surface area (P_e) is proportional to the fourth power of the absolute temperature, T, of the body; in equation form:

$$P_e = e\sigma T^4 \dotfill 1)$$

The quantity σ is a universal constant known as the *Stefan-Boltzmann constant*, and e is called the *emissivity* of the surface which can have values ranging from 0 to 1, depending on the nature of the surface. (Very black surfaces have e close to 1 and are good radiators, whereas shiny reflecting surfaces are poor emitters of radiation with e close to zero.)

If a body only radiated energy, then it would eventually cool to a temperature of absolute zero if it were not at the same time being supplied with energy. However, bodies also absorb energy which is being radiated by other objects in their surroundings and so will only cool to a temperature at which its rate of energy emission is equal to its rate of energy absorption. When this temperature is reached, the body is in thermal equilibrium with its surroundings and this only occurs when its temperature is equal to that of the surroundings. Whereas the rate of emission of radiant energy depends on the absolute temperature of the body, its rate of absorption of energy (P_a) depends on the absolute temperature of its surroundings (T_r), that is:

$$P_a = e\,\sigma\,T_r^{\,4} \quad\ldots\ldots\ldots\ldots\ldots\ldots\ldots\ldots\ldots\ 2)$$

Thus, for a body at temperature T surrounded by walls at a temperature T_r, the net rate of loss (or gain) of radiant energy per unit area is:

$$P = P_e - P_a = e\,\sigma(T^4 - T_r^4) \quad\ldots\ldots\ldots\ldots\ldots\ldots\ 3)$$

Note that there is no net loss (or gain) of energy when $T = T_r$. If the body is constantly maintained at a much higher temperature than its surroundings ($T \gg T_r$), then $P_e \gg P_a$ and $P \approx P_e$, in which case we can ignore the absorption of radiation from its surroundings. Otherwise, we must also account for the absorption of radiation using eqn. 3).

In this experiment we shall examine the dependence of radiant energy on the temperature of the radiating body. In one measurement we shall use a high-temperature source, for which $T \gg T_r$, and in a low-temperature measurement we shall employ a surface heated to temperatures only about 100°C above room temperature. According to the Stefan-Boltzman law, a plot of P -vs- $(T^4 - T_r^4)$ (or P -vs- T^4 if $T \gg T_r$) should yield a straight line.

B. Radiation Detector

To measure the relative intensity of the radiation emitted by a source, a miniature *thermopile* (a set of thermocouples made of very fine wires) is used which produces a small output voltage proportional to its net rate of gain of radiant energy. When not actively taking measurements it is important that the detector be shielded from the radiation source so that its temperature remains the same as that of the room. A sheet of insulating material can be inserted between the detector and source when not recording a measurement.

If the temperature of the detector were at absolute zero, it would produce a voltage directly proportional to the intensity of radiation incident upon it. However, since the detector is at room temperature it is also radiating energy and the voltage produced is proportional to the difference between its rate of absorption of radiation from the source and its own rate of emission, i.e., to the net rate of change $P = e\,\sigma(T^4 - T_r^4)$. As noted previously, for the high-temperature measurements $T \gg T_r$ and we can assume $P = e\,\sigma T^4$ (eqn. 1). For low-temperature measurements, however, we cannot ignore the detector's own emission of radiation and must use eqn. 3.

Note that the detector does not measure the net radiant power in absolute units (watts) but instead provides an output in millivolts which is proportional to the power.

Procedure

Part A. High-Temperature Measurements

A hot lamp filament is used for the high-temperature study. The temperature of the filament can be varied by adjusting the voltage across the bulb. A temperature near 3000 K is reached with a voltage of about 12v.

To determine the temperature of the filament we make use of the known dependence of the electrical resistance of the filament on its temperature. The resistance R of the filament can be determined from Ohm's law:

$$R = \frac{V}{i} \quad \dotfill \text{4)}$$

where V is the voltage and i the electric current in the filament, both of which are directly measurable. If R_r is the resistance of the filament at room temperature (T_r) and R is its resistance at temperature T, then the difference in resistance ΔR (= $R-R_r$) due to the change in temperature ΔT (= $T-T_r$) is given by the expression:

$$\frac{\Delta R}{R_r} = \alpha \, \Delta T$$

where α is the *temperature coefficient of resistance* for the filament wire. For the lamp used in this study, $\alpha = 4.5 \times 10^{-3} \, K^{-1}$. Rearranging this equation, we have:

$$T = \frac{1}{\alpha}\left(\frac{R}{R_r} - 1\right) + T_r \quad K$$

$$\text{or} \quad T = 222\left(\frac{R}{R_r} - 1\right) + T_r \quad K \dotfill \text{5)}$$

in which $1/\alpha$ is replaced by its numerical value.

WARNING: Do not allow the voltage across the lamp to
exceed 12v. Higher voltages will burn out the filament.

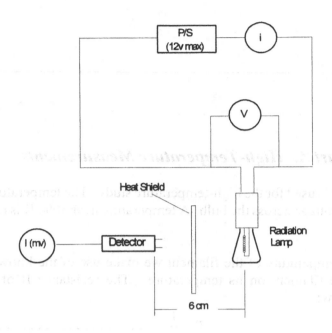

Figure 1. *Experimental arrangement for high-temperature measurements.*

i)   Set up the experimental arrangement shown in fig. 1. DO NOT turn on the power supply yet. The detector should be at the same height as the lamp filament and carefully aligned with it.

ii)   Measure and record the room temperature (T_r) and convert this to the kelvin scale.

You will also need to determine the resistance of the filament at room temperature (R_r) for use in later calculations of the filament temperature (eqn. 5). This can be done using Ohm's law but to avoid significant heating of the filament it is important that the voltage across the lamp filament not exceed 0.100 volt. Switch on the power supply. Slowly raise the voltage to this value and quickly record the corresponding current in amperes. Compute the resistance R_r and enter your results in Table I.

IMPORTANT: Be careful not to move the detector and lamp
during the following measurements.

iii)   With the lamp voltage at V = 1 volt, record the current i in the filament then remove the heat shield and measure the relative intensity P of the detected radiation in millivolts. Replace the heat shield. Repeat this for lamp voltages up to V = 12v in 1v steps. Make your detector readings quickly, and between readings keep the heat shield between the lamp and detector so that the detector is not appreciably heated by the lamp.

Analysis (A)

i)   Calculate the resistance R of the filament at each voltage setting, entering the value in Table I.

ii)   Calculate (eqn. 5) the corresponding temperatures and enter these values also in the Table.

iii)   To test the Stefan-Boltzmann law (eqn. 1), we shall assume the intensity of radiation P and the absolute temperature T are related by a general power law of the form:

$$P = aT^n$$

where 'a' and n are constants. If we take logs both sides of this equation, then a plot of log P -vs.- log T should yield a straight line with slope equal to n. In Table I, tabulate log P and log T and plot this graph, being sure to choose appropriate axis scales so that the data points span the full size of the graph paper. (You will need to suppress the origin for this.) Determine the slope of your graph. How well does this agree with the Stefan-Boltzmann law of radiation (n = 4)?

Part B. Low-Temperature Measurements

For low-temperature studies a hollow *radiation cube* is used with four different types of surfaces having different emissivities. Only the black surface will be used for these measurements. The cube can be heated from room temperature to about 120°C by means of an electric lamp inside the cube. The temperature is measured using a thermistor which is embedded in the cube. The electrical resistance of the thermistor does not change linearly with temperature like the metal filament and Table A shows corresponding values of temperature for a range of resistance values. The thermistor resistance will be measured directly using a digital ohmmeter and the values converted to a temperature measurement with the aid of this table.

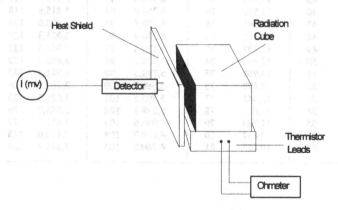

Figure 2. Experimental arrangement for low-temperature measurements.

iv)   Set up the experiment as shown in fig. 2. DO NOT switch on the heating lamp at this time. The detector should be pointing directly at the center of the black surface of the cube and about 3 to4cm away. Be careful again not to change the relative positions of the detector and cube during the following measurements.

v)   Measure and record the room temperature (T_r) and convert this to the kelvin scale.

vi)   With the heat shield in place, turn on the heating lamp in the cube and set the power switch to its maximum setting. When the thermistor resistance indicates the temperature to be about 10°C above room temperature (use Table A), turn the power off to slow down the temperature rise. When the temperature has nearly leveled off, record the new thermistor resistance and the detector reading P in millivolts. These readings should be taken together while only briefly removing the heat shield. Record also the corresponding temperature to the nearest 1°C from Table A.

vii)   Repeat the procedure of step vi) at approximately 10°C intervals until the temperature of the cube reaches about 110°C.

Table A: *Thermistor resistance versus temperature*

Therm. Res. (Ω)	Temp. (°C)	Therm. Res. (Ω)	Temp. (°C)	Therm. Res. (Ω)	Temp. (°C)	Therm. Res. (Ω)	Temp. (°C)	Therm. Res. (Ω)	Temp. (°C)	Therm. Res. (Ω)	Temp. (°C)
207,850	10	66,356	34	24,415	58	10,110	82	4,615.1	106	2,281.0	130
197,560	11	63,480	35	23,483	59	9,767.2	83	4,475.0	107	2,218.3	131
187,840	12	60,743	36	22,590	60	9,437.7	84	4,339.7	108	2,157.6	132
178,650	13	58,138	37	21,736	61	9,120.8	85	4,209.1	109	2,098.7	133
169,950	14	55,658	38	20,919	62	8,816.0	86	4,082.9	110	2,041.7	134
161,730	15	53,297	39	20,136	63	8,522.7	87	3,961.1	111	1,986.4	135
153,950	16	51,048	40	19,386	64	8,240.6	88	3,843.4	112	1,932.8	136
146,580	17	48,905	41	18,668	65	7,969.1	89	3,729.7	113	1,880.9	137
139,610	18	46,863	42	17,980	66	7,707.7	90	3,619.8	114	1,830.5	138
133,000	19	44,917	43	17,321	67	7,456.2	91	3,513.6	115	1,781.7	139
126,740	20	43,062	44	16,689	68	7,214.0	92	3,411.0	116	1,734.3	140
120,810	21	41,292	45	16,083	69	6,980.6	93	3,311.8	117	1,688.4	141
115,190	22	39,605	46	15,502	70	6,755.9	94	3,215.8	118	1,643.9	142
109,850	23	37,995	47	14,945	71	6,539.4	95	3,123.0	119	1,600.6	143
104,800	24	36,458	48	14,410	72	6,330.8	96	3,033.3	120	1,558.7	144
100,000	25	34,991	49	13,897	73	6,129.8	97	2,946.5	121	1,518.0	145
95,447	26	33,591	50	13,405	74	5,936.1	98	2,862.5	122	1,478.6	146
91,126	27	32,253	51	12,932	75	5,749.3	99	2,781.3	123	1,440.2	147
87,022	28	30,976	52	12,479	76	5,569.3	100	2,702.7	124	1,403.0	148
83,124	29	29,756	53	12,043	77	5,395.6	101	2,626.6	125	1,366.9	149
79,422	30	28,590	54	11,625	78	5,228.1	102	2,553.0	126	1,331.9	150
75,903	31	27,475	55	11,223	79	5,066.6	103	2,481.7	127		
72,560	32	26,409	56	10,837	80	4,910.7	104	2,412.6	128		
69,380	33	25,390	57	10,467	81	4,760.3	105	2,345.8	129		

Analysis (B)

i)   Complete the remaining temperature columns in Table II.

ii)   Construct a graph of P -vs.- $(T^4 - T_r^4)$. How well does your graph display a linear relationship, as predicted by the Stefan- Boltzmann law?

Questions

1.   In analyzing the high-temperature results, it was assumed that the detector's own emission of radiation at temperature T_r was negligibly small compared with its absorption of radiation from the lamp. Check this by calculating $(T^4 - T_r^4)$ for three temperatures within your range of measured temperatures T (choose a low, medium, and high value of T). What are the percentage differences between these 'correct' values and the assumed values T^4? Calculate $\log (T^4 - T_r^4)$ for these three temperatures. Was the neglect of the T_r^4 term justified for all temperatures?

2.   In your low-temperature study, what differences in the intensity readings would you expect had you detected radiation from the shiny, reflecting surface of the cube instead of the black surface?

3.   Discuss the importance of using the heat shield between measurements. How might its absence have affected your results?

4.   What other information would you need to know in your experiment in order to determine a value for the Stefan-Boltzmann universal constant?

Name: _____   . Partner(s): _____

_____

Table I. High-temperature measurements

$$T_r = \qquad °C = \underline{\hspace{2cm}} K$$

$$V = 0.100 \text{ volt}; \quad i_r = \quad \text{amp.}; \quad \therefore R_r (= V/i_r) = \underline{\hspace{2cm}} \text{ ohms}$$

V (volt)	i (amp)	I (mv)	R = V/i (ohm)	T * (K)	ℓn I	ℓn T
1.0						
2.0						
3.0						
4.0						
5.0						
6.0						
7.0						
8.0						
9.0						
10.0						
11.0						

$$*\quad T = 222\left(\frac{R}{R_r} - 1\right) + T_r, \quad K$$

Table II: Low-temperature measurements

$$T_r = \qquad °C = \underline{\hspace{2cm}} K; \quad \therefore \quad T_r^4 = \underline{\hspace{2cm}} \times 10^9 \ (K^4)$$

R ($\times 10^3$) ohm	I (mv)	T (°C)	T (K)	T^4 ($\times 10^9$) (K^4)	($T^4 - T_r^4$) $\times 10^9$ (K^4)

Signature of Instructor: _____

Cathode Ray Oscilloscope 15

*The principal features and method of operation of a cathode
ray oscilloscope will be examined. The instrument will be
used to measure several different voltage waveforms.*

Introduction

Many devices used in measurements provide an output in the form of a voltage signal. If the
output is a steady (DC) signal, or very nearly so, a moving pointer meter may be usually satisfactory
for recording the voltage level. If, on the other hand, the voltage changes with time (an AC signal)
at a frequency much greater than about 0.5 hz, such a meter is unsuitable since the inertia of the
pointer and its associated mechanical parts is too great to follow the torque variation produced in the
meter by the changing voltage. At best, such a meter can only provide information on some average
voltage level.

A cathode-ray oscilloscope (CRO) is an instrument which is capable of providing detailed
information on the time dependence of a voltage signal, and it does so in the form of a graph of
instantaneous voltage -vs.- time. This graph is "plotted" by a beam of fast-moving electrons which,
in view of their negligible inertia, can respond almost instantaneously to any rapidly changing voltage.
Voltage levels down to a millivolt which change in a nanosecond or less can easily be displayed on an
oscilloscope. Because of its versatility, the CRO in one form or another has found applications in just
about every area of science and technology.

The conventional CRO consists of the following components:

- *Cathode-ray tube (CRT)*
- *Vertical (or Y-) deflection amplifier*
- *Horizontal (or X-) deflection amplifier*
- *Linear sweep (or timebase) generator*
- *Synchronization circuit*
- *Power supplies*

A. Cathode Ray Tube

The heart of a CRO is the *cathode-ray tube* (CRT), which is an evacuated glass tube containing
a number of elements, as shown in Fig. 1. Electrons are emitted from a hot cathode (K) which is
heated by the filament (F). These electrons are then accelerated toward a cylindrical anode (A_2) held
at a high positive potential of several thousand volts relative to the cathode. After passing through A_2

the electrons continue at high speed (~ 10^7 m/sec) to the screen (S). This is coated on the inside with a phosphor which glows wherever the electrons strike it, and if the beam is well focused a bright spot of light will be seen at the front of the tube. It is on this screen that the plot of signal voltage-versus-time is presented. Beam focusing is provided by the first anode (A_1) and the intensity of the light spot on the screen (which depends on the beam intensity) is controlled by the grid (G) just beyond the cathode. The arrangement provided by F-K-G-A1-A2 is referred to as the *electron gun* and the voltage levels for its various elements are provided by a power supply built into the oscilloscope.

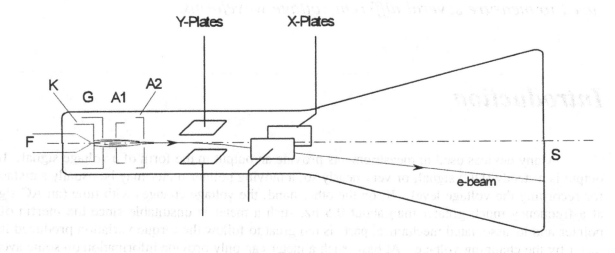

Figure 1: Principal Components of a cathode-ray tube

Two pairs of electrodes called *deflection plates* are positioned between the electron gun and the screen. If a voltage difference is applied between either pair of plates an electric field is set up which serves to deflect the electrons, the beam therefore striking the screen off-center. The two sets of plates are oriented perpendicular to each other so that one set produces a vertical deflection of the beam (the Y-deflection plates) and the other set produces a horizontal deflection (the X-deflection plates). In this way the beam may be deflected to any point on the screen.

Usually the voltage signal which we wish to examine is applied to the Y-plates either directly or, if the signal is weak, through an *amplifier* which is referred to as the vertical or Y-amplifier. This provides a vertical deflection of the spot on the screen which depends on the magnitude of the applied voltage. If the voltage varies with time (an AC signal) then the spot moves up and down, following the variation of the applied voltage. Providing this voltage changes only slowly then the changes in position of the spot on the screen can be followed by eye. At frequencies in excess of about 10 Hz, however, the persistence of vision of the eye and the persistence (or *afterglow*) of the phosphor cause the moving spot to appear as a continuous vertical line on the screen and information on the time dependence of the applied signal becomes lost. To circumvent this difficulty the horizontal deflection plates are also brought into use. If a second voltage is applied to the X-plates which increases linearly with time, then the spot moves horizontally across the screen at constant speed while at the same time it responds to any vertical changes in position caused by the input signal. The result is a graph of the input voltage signal-versus-time displayed on the screen.

B. Linear Timebase and Synchronization

The voltage applied to the X-plates has the form shown in figure 2. This is known as a *linear timebase* or *sawtooth voltage*.

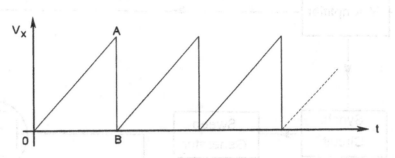

Figure 2: *Sawtooth voltage applied to CRT X-plates.*

The section of the waveform OA causes the beam to move at constant horizontal speed from left to right across the screen. Between AB the voltage drops suddenly back to its value at 0, causing the beam to rapidly retrace its path to the left of the screen, after which it repeats its linear excursion to the right. Although this retrace, or *flyback*, occurs very rapidly it nevertheless requires a finite time. In most oscilloscopes the beam is turned off during this small time interval so that the flyback trace is not observed. The circuit which generates the timebase voltage is built into the oscilloscope and is called a *linear sweep generator* since its function is to sweep the beam horizontally across the screen at constant rate.

If a periodic (repetitive) voltage signal is applied to the Y-plates, the timebase voltage can be made to vary with the same frequency as the input signal so that it sweeps uniformly across the screen in just one cycle of the input signal. In this way one cycle of the input signal is traced out on the screen over and over again. Alternatively, the horizontal sweep frequency may be adjusted so as to encompass any number of cycles of the vertical input signal to allow more than one cycle to be observed on the screen. In order to accommodate a wide range of possible input signal frequencies, the frequency of the sweep generator must itself be adjustable over a wide range of values.

To maintain a stationary display of the input waveform on the screen, it is necessary to synchronize the timebase generator with the input signal. This is achieved by feeding a small portion of the input signal to a *synchronizing circuit*, the output of which is used to drive the sweep generator so that its frequency becomes "locked" to the input signal frequency. When properly adjusted, the timebase is said to be *synchronized*. Occasionally it is useful if the timebase can be synchronized to a source other than the input signal and most oscilloscopes also have provision for external synchronization.

Instead of applying the timebase voltage to the X-plates of the oscilloscope one may wish to apply a second external signal. This can be accomplished through the horizontal, or X-amplifier, in much the same way as for the Y-input signal. This method of operation is employed, for example, when comparing frequencies of two separate voltage signals using Lissajous patterns.

A simplified block diagram showing the essential components of the oscilloscope is shown in fig. 3.

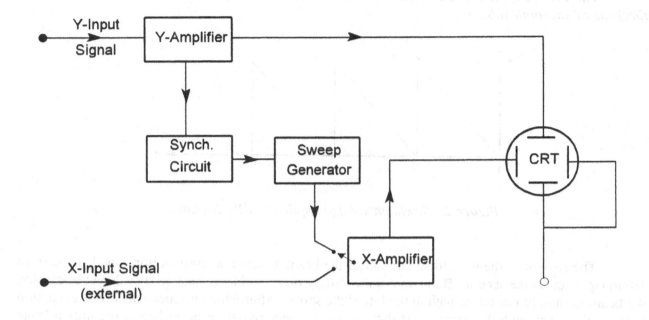

Figure 3: Block diagram of a CRO.

Procedure

The objective of this experiment is to gain experience in using an oscilloscope and to obtain familiarity with its various controls and measurement techniques. We shall examine some basic measurement techniques using both sinusoidal and non-sinusoidal AC voltages. The AC signals are obtained from a variable audio oscillator (AO) which can generate sinusoidal-, square- and triangular-shaped voltage waveforms. The CRO instructions below refer to the BK Precision model 2120B oscilloscope which is shown in fig. 4. This is a dual-beam trace instrument with two vertical amplifiers and a timebase for horizontal sweep.

> *NOTE: When the CRO is used to measure absolute values of voltage or time intervals, it is important that the scale multipliers for the vertical amplifier or timebase be set to their calibrated positions (x1). Other settings may be used for general observation but **not** for precise measurements.*

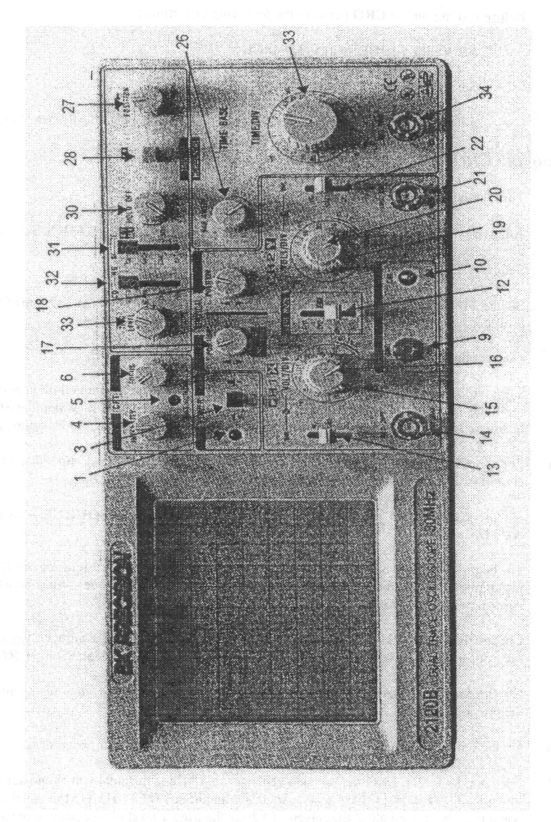

Figure 4. *BK Precision model 2120B CRO.*

i) <u>Before</u> turning on the **CRO** perform the following operations:

-- Set **VERT MODE** switch [12] to **CH1**.
-- Set **AC/GND/DC** switch [13] to **GND**.
-- Set Trigger **COUPLING** switch [32] to **AUTO**.
-- Set Trigger **SOURCE** switch [31] to **CH1**.
-- Set all controls with pointers [4,6,33,30,27,17,18,26] to be vertically straight up.

Using the CRO to Measure Frequency

ii) Turn on the **CRO** by pushing in the **POWER** button [3].

iii) Adjust trace's brightness and sharpness using the **CRT INTENSITY** and **FOCUS** controls [4,6].

iv) Set the **VAR SWEEP** control [26] to calibrate i.e. fully clockwise.

v) Set the **TIME/DIV** to 1S. A spot should be seen moving across the screen at a rate of 1 division (cm) per second. Check this sweep rate with a timer and record your result.

vi) Connect the cable from the function generator to the input for CH1 [14].

vii) Turn on the function generator, set the frequency to 1 Hz (1 on the range button and 1 on the multiplier), set the amplitude to minimum (fully counterclockwise), and set wave shape (function) to square wave. (If the function generator has a DC offset, set it to the middle – zero.)

viii) For the CH1 amplifier, set the **VOLT/DIV** control to 1V and make sure that the smaller control is turned fully clockwise (calibrated position) and is not pulled out.

ix) Set the **AC/GND/DC** switch [13] to **DC** and the **COUPLING SOURCE** switch [32] to **AUTO**.

x) The beam spot should be jumping between two vertical positions with a frequency of 1 Hz. Adjust the amplitude of the function generator so that the waveform takes up one vertical division. (Use vertical position control [17].)

xi) Change the **TIME/DIV** to 1 mS and set the function generator to 1kHz output. <u>Reproduce</u> the trace observed on the screen in your lab book and <u>record</u> the function generator and **CRO** settings.

xii) On the function generator switch to a <u>triangular wave</u> and record your observations as in the previous step.

xiii) On the function generator switch to a <u>sinusoidal wave</u> and record your observations.

xiv) Now set the frequency of the function generator to 5 kHz (sinusoidal wave) and set the **CRO** timebase **TIME/DIV** [33] to 0.1 mS. Adjust the amplifier **VOLT/DIV** [15] so that the observed wave fills about one-half of the screen. (Adjust the trigger level if necessary to obtain a stable trace.) Change the amplitude control to observe its effect on the trace.

xv)   Measure the period T of the observed waveform, using as many full waveforms as appear on the screen. Calculate the frequency of the waveform ($\nu = 1/T$). Describe the agreement of the determined frequency with that of the setting of the function generator. Reproduce the observed trace in your lab book, together with the settings for the function generator and the CRO.

xvi) Record the trace patterns observed on the screen when the timebase is changed from 0.1 mS to 20 μS and then to 2 μS. **Explain** the observed patterns.

xvii) Reset the timebase to 0.1 mS and increase the frequency of the function generator to 10 kHz and then 50 kHz. Record the trace patterns observed at these frequency settings.

AC- and DC-Coupled Input Signals

An input signal may be either AC- or DC-coupled to the Y-plates of a CRO. When AC-coupled, any constant (i.e. DC) voltage level in the signal is blocked from reaching the Y-plates while time-varying AC components in the signal (if present) are allowed through. When DC-coupled, both DC and AC components are allowed through to the plates. If it is necessary to measure the DC voltage level, the input signal must then be DC-coupled to the CRO.

Occasionally, small AC "ripple" voltages may be superimposed on an otherwise steady DC voltage signal. This can be the case, for example, with the output from an unfiltered DC power supply. Since the amplitude of the ripple is usually only a small fraction of the DC voltage, the Y-amplification must usually be increased in order to study it. To prevent the beam from moving off screen due to the larger DC component the DC voltage must be blocked from the Y-plates, i.e., the input signal must then be AC-coupled to the CRO.

xviii) Set the vertical amplifier to 5 V/div, the timebase to 0.1 mS, and the trigger to **AUTO**.

xix)   Connect the DC power supply to the **CRO**.

xx)   Align the trace at the center of the screen either with the DC power supply switched off or setting the amplifier of the **CRO** to **GND**. This provides a zero voltage reference line on the screen.

xxi)   The output provided by the power supply can be set to any DC level in the range of about zero to 12 volts by means of an adjustable control having unmarked scale settings. Switch on the power supply and calibrate it at each scale setting from minimum to maximum. Organize your results in a table of scale settings versus output voltage (as measured by the **CRO**).

xxii) If there is also superimposed on the DC output some low amplitude noise or "ripple" voltage, this will probably need to be amplified in order to measure it and for this purpose the larger DC input signal must be AC-coupled to the T-amplifier. Set the input signal to AC-couple and the amplifier to 10 mV/div.

xxiii) By adjusting the Y-amplification and the timebase setting, determine whether the ripple voltage is random or periodic. (If necessary adjust the trigger level to obtain a stable trace.) If it is seen to be periodic, adjust the timebase until just one or two full cycles of the ripple voltage are seen and measure its frequency. Can you identify the probable source of this noise. Measure also the amplitude (peak-to-peak) of the ripple voltage when the output from the power supply is set close to zero, mid-range and then full-scale. How does the output voltage affect the noise amplitude? Sketch the shape of the ripple when the DC voltage is set for maximum output.

Lissajous Patterns

If two AC voltage sources have frequencies which are not too different, the ratio of the frequencies may be measured using the Lissajous method providing one frequency can be varied. In the present experiment, a 60 Hz (sine wave) transformer will be used to calibrate a function generator in the frequency range 30 - 210 Hz.

xxiv) Set the frequency of the function generator to 60 Hz (sine wave) and connect it to the **CH1** amplifier. Connect the 6.3 volt, 60 Hz AC source (transformer) to the **CH2** amplifier.

xxv) Set **VERT MODE** to **CH1**. Change **TIME/DIV** until there are 3 or 4 complete cycles on the screen and adjust the **VOLT/DIV** for **CH1** so that the amplitude nearly fills the screen.

xxvi) Change the **VERT MODE** to **CH2**. Adjust the **VOLT/DIV** for **CH2** so that the amplitude nearly fills the screen.

xxvii) Press in the **X-Y** button on the **TRIGGER** panel. (The coupling source and vertical mode controls should be set for differnet channels.)

xxviii) Adjust the frequency to obtain a stable "circular" trace. (Since the relative phases are not locked, the trace will tend to slowly rotate through a series of ellipses as it goes through 360 degrees.) Record the Lissajous pattern observed for the frequency ratio of 1:1, and also the frequency reading of the function generator.

xxix) Calibrate the scale of the function generator over the frequency range 30-210 Hz at the following settings corresponding to Lissajous patterns:

v_1 : 30   60   90   120   150   180   210

v_1/v_2 : 1/2   1/1   3/2   2/1   5/2   3/1   7/2

(v_2 = line frequency, 60 hz)

Sketch the Lissajous pattern observed at each of these frequency ratios.

Speed of Sound *16*

*Two different methods will be used to measure the speed of
sound in air at audible and ultrasonic frequencies.*

Introduction

Sound waves are longitudinal mechanical waves and therefore require a medium in which to propagate. Particles of the medium transmitting such a wave oscillate in the direction of propagation of the wave itself. Audible sound waves are longitudinal mechanical waves whose frequencies lie in the range of approximately 20Hz to 20,000Hz (or 20kHz). Within this range, the human ear and brain can be stimulated to give the sensation of hearing. Longitudinal mechanical waves with frequencies above the audible range are called ultrasonic waves, whereas those whose frequencies fall below the audible range are called infrasonic waves. In this experiment we shall measure the velocity of sound in air at frequencies near 1kHz (audible region) and 40kHz (ultrasonic region).

The speed of sound in a gas can be expressed by the relationship:

$$v = \sqrt{\frac{\gamma\, RT}{M}} \qquad \text{1)}$$

where γ is a constant for the particular gas (equal to the ratio of its specific heats at constant pressure and constant volume), R is the universal gas constant, M the molar mass (kg/mol) of the gas, and T is its absolute temperature (Kelvin).

We see from this equation that the speedy of sound in any gas is directly proportional to the square root of the absolute temperature and is independent of the gas pressure. Furthermore, if the speed of sound in a gas is known at one temperature, then it can be computed for any other temperature, since it follows from eqn. 1) that:

$$\frac{v_1}{v_2} = \sqrt{\frac{T_1}{T_2}} \qquad \text{2)}$$

The measured velocity of sound in air at 0°C (273 K) is 331.5 m/s. Its value in air at any other absolute temperature T is, therefore, given by:

$$v_{air} = 331.5 \sqrt{\frac{T}{273}} \quad \text{m/s} \qquad \text{3)}$$

The sound waves are generated in this experiment by transducers, which are devices that convert electrical energy into mechanical energy and vice versa. If a transducer is driven with an electrical signal of given frequency (e.g., from an audio oscillator), it will undergo a mechanical vibration at the same frequency. The air adjacent to the transducer therefore becomes alternately compressed and rarified by the vibration, and this disturbance is transmitted outward from the source as a sound wave through the air with the same frequency as that of the source. Since tranducers are reversible we may also use a second identical one to act as a detector. When a sound wave is incident on this second transducer, the pressure variations in the wave will now induce in it a mechanical vibration of the same frequency. This, in turn, is converted into an electrical signal whose voltage level and frequency can be studied using an oscilloscope.

To determine the velocity of sound, v, we make use of the relationship:

$$v = \lambda f \qquad\qquad 4)$$

where λ is the wavelength of the sound wave and f is its frequency. Since the frequency of the sound wave is the same as that of the audio oscillator, its measurement with an oscilloscope is quite straightforward. In determining the wavelength we shall use two different methods according to the frequency range under study.

Method 1: Audible Sound Waves

A sound wave traveling in an air-filled tube closed at each end will undergo reflections at each end of the tube, giving rise to two traveling waves moving in opposite directions. The resultant wave in the tube is determined according to the principle of superposition and may be very complex. However, just as in the case of transverse waves on a vibrating string, stationary longitudinal waves can be set up in the air column, i.e., a condition of resonance. The ends of the tube must correspond to positions of displacement nodes since the air molecules are unable to freely undergo displacements there. Resonance will therefore occur if the wavelength of the sound wave is such that a whole number of half-wavelengths "fit" into the length L of tube, i.e., providing -

$$L = n\frac{\lambda}{2} = n\frac{v}{2f} \quad , \quad \text{where } n = 1, 2, 3 \ldots, \text{etc.} \qquad 5)$$

Exactly the same requirement is found necessary for establishing stationary transverse waves on a vibrating string. Just as a string vibrates with a set of n loops, so does the air column vibrate in n segments at resonance, with the molecules undergoing their maximum displacements causing maximum sound intensity at the center of each segment (the displacement antinodes). The wavelengths corresponding to the first four harmonics (n = 1, 2, 3 and 4) are depicted in fig. 1.

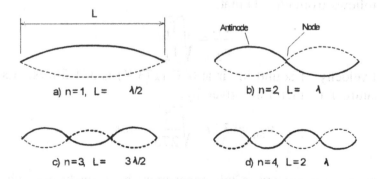

a) n=1, L= λ/2   b) n=2, L= λ

c) n=3, L= 3λ/2   d) n=4, L=2 λ

Figure 1: *Standing sound waves corresponding to first four harmonics in a closed tube. Note that the integer n corresponds to the number of half wavelengths in the tube.*

The experimental arrangement is shown in fig. 2. The resonance tube, of a design named after the scientist Kundt, has at one end a speaker S which is driven by an audio-frequency oscillator (AFO). This acts as the source of sound waves in the tube. The AFO output is also sent to the Y1 amplifier of a cathode ray oscilloscope (CRO). A small movable microphone (M), located a short distance from S and powered by a switched battery (SW), is attached to a thin rod inside the tube and serves as a sound detector. This generates a voltage whose amplitude depends on the intensity of sound at its location. This voltage is fed to the Y2 amplifier of the CRO. The CRO can therefore display both the generated waveform and the detected waveform. The Kundt tube has a movable plunger (P) at its other end and as it is moved along the tube the amplitude of the microphone signal on the CRO is seen to vary. When P is located to produce a resonance in the tube (i.e., when eqn. 5 is satisfied) then the microphone detects a maximum signal. Resonance is thus determined using the CRO to observe positions of P which give maximum amplitude voltages from the microphone.

Suppose a resonance is initially detected with P located at x_i. If P is then moved to the next resonance position it must have moved through a distance equal to one-half wavelength. If it moves through 'm' such resonances to a final location at x_f, then the total distance moved is:

$$x_f - x_i = m\frac{\lambda}{2}$$

6)

Equation 6) can therefore be used to determine λ. The frequency of the sound wave is just that of the AFO and can be determined by measuring the period T of the AFO signal with the CRO (i.e. $f = 1/T$). With λ and f known, the velocity of sound can be determined from eqn. 4).

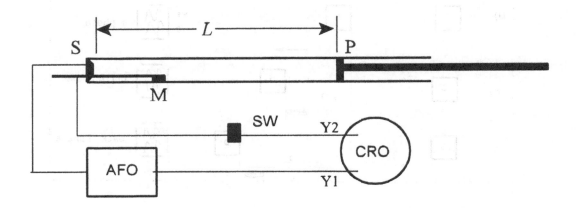

Figure 2: Acoustic resonance tube.

Method 2: Ultrasonic Waves

In measuring the velocity of sound in the ultrasonic region we shall use a different technique. In this case we observe directly the relative phase between the sound wave at the source and the sound wave on its arrival at the detector. Suppose the detector is initially positioned so that the wave has the same phase at the detector as it has at the source (i.e., phase angle difference equals 0°). If the detector is now moved away from the source, the phase difference will change by 2π radians each time the detector moves through a distance equal to one wavelength. Whenever the separation changes by a whole number of wavelengths, therefore, the detected and emitted signals will be in phase.

We can observe the relative phase between the two signals using a dual-trace oscilloscope. In this case, the source and detected signals are fed to the Y-plates of the oscilloscope via separate amplifiers (Y1 and Y2) and each signal waveform is separately displayed on the CRO (see fig. 4(a)). The detector is positioned so that the two waveforms are initially in phase. By moving the detector slowly away from the source, the distance through which it must be moved before the waveforms are again in phase can then be measured. The phase changes which the detector waveform undergoes when it is moved through a distance equal to one wavelength are depicted in figs. 4(b) to 4(d).

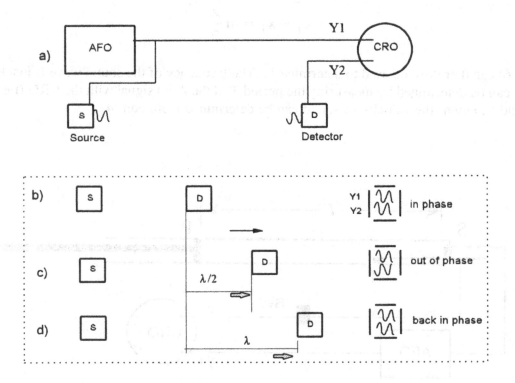

Figure 4:   *(a) General arrangement to study the relative phase between the source and detector transducer waveforms. (b) The source and detector are initially positioned so that their waveforms displayed on the CRO are in phase. (c) As the detector is moved away from the source its waveform becomes out of phase with that of the source. d) After moving through a distance of one wavelength the source and detector waveforms are again back in phase.*

Procedure

Method 1: Audible Stationary Sound Waves

i)   Set up the arrangement shown in Fig. 2 with the output from the AFO connected to both the speaker S and the input for the Y1 amplifier.

ii)   The small microphone is placed a few centimeters from the speaker. Connect its cable to the second Y2 CRO input. Turn on the microphone switch (SW).

iii)   Set the initial settings for the CRO and AFO as follows:

CRO		**AFO**
Y1-Amplifier:	100 mV/div	Sinewave Output
	AC coupled	1kHz frequency
Y2-Amplifier:	10 mV/div	Max. Output
	AC coupled	
Time Base:	100 μS /div	
	Auto Trig	
	Calibrated	

iv)   Set the AFO frequency to about 1000 Hz and adjust the amplitude on the audio oscillator so that the sound can be heard. Positioning the plunger P will cause the sound to change in loudness. Adjust its position to obtain a maximum sound intensity (i.e., to obtain a resonance condition) and record its position, x_i (see Table I).

v)   Now observe the AFO waveform signal and adjust the Y1 gain on the CRO so that the waveform fills about half the CRO screen. Make any necessary adjustments to the CRO controls to obtain a stable display of this waveform.

vi)   Measure the frequency of the AFO waveform using the CRO. First check that the timebase is set for calibrated sweep and then make any suitable adjustments to the sweep settings until a convenient number of complete oscillations is observed on the screen (say about 10 oscillations for 1000 Hz). Measure the total time t for this number of oscillations. If the number of complete oscillations is p, then the period of the waveform is just $T= t/p$. Determine T and record the corresponding frequency f (=1/T).

vii)   Now switch to the microphone waveform signal on the CRO. Increase the Y2 gain on the CRO until the signal fills about half the screen for this initial standing wave condition. Make any necessary adjustments to the CRO controls to obtain a stable display of this waveform.

viii)   Move the plunger along the tube, observing the changes in amplitude of the microphone signal. Each time this amplitude goes through a maximum value a new resonance condition is achieved in the tube. Record the final position x_f and the number of new resonances observed, m.

ix)   Calculate the wavelength of the sound wave using eqn. 6) and the speed of sound from eqn. 5).

x)   Repeat steps v) to ix) for frequencies of 1500, 2000, 2500, and 3000 Hz.

Method 2: Relative Phase between Ultrasonic Waves

Two quartz crystal transducers are used to generate and detect a sound wave in the ultrasonic range.   A characteristic of such transducers is their ability to operate only in a narrow band of frequencies (in this case near 40 kHz), their efficiencies dropping rapidly to zero within about ±1kHz of their operating frequency.

xi)   Mount the two transducers on an optical bench so that they face each other with a separation of about 10 cm. and lock the source transducer in position. The general arrangement is shown in Fig. 4(a). The output from the audio oscillator is fed to the source transducer and also to the Y1-amplifier of the CRO. The detector is connected to the Y2-amplifier of the CRO. Initial settings for these instruments are as follows:

CRO		AFO
Y1-Amplifier:	5 V/div.	Sinewave Output
	AC coupled	40 khz frequency
Y2-Amplifier:	50 mV/div.	Max. Output
	AC coupled	
Time Base:	100 µs/div.	
	Auto Trig.	
	x1 Multiplier	

Make any necessary adjustments to the CRO to obtain a stable display of the AFO (Y1) waveform.

xii)   If the AFO driving frequency is set outside the narrow band of operating frequencies for these transducers, there will be no sound wave generated and therefore no detected signal. In this case the Y2-signal on the CRO screen appears simply as a horizontal line. To obtain a Y2 signal, carefully tune the AFO output frequency (near 40 kHz) until a detected waveform appears. When the amplitude of this signal is maximized the transducers are operating at their proper efficiencies.

xiii)   Move the detector until the transmitted (Y1) and detected (Y2) waveforms are in phase. (*NOTE:* you may alternatively use the method of Lissajous figures, frequency ratio 1:1, to perform this measurement.) Record the position of the detector on the optical bench scale. Now slowly move the detector away from the source through a distance of 10λ. Record the new position of the detector. Repeat this measurement at least five times using different initial positions of the detector (see Table II). From these data calculate the average distance, $\bar{d}$, corresponding to ten wavelengths and determine from this the wavelength of the ultrasonic sound wave.

xiv)   Determine the AFO (Y1) frequency f for the source waveform by measuring its period τ on the oscilloscope. Be sure the time base multiplier is calibrated for this measurement.

Analysis

Method 1

i)   Calculate the average value for the speed of sound determined from Method 1 and compare this with the accepted value corrected for temperature (see eqn. 3). Do the two agree within your estimated experimental uncertainty?

Method 2

ii)   Calculate the speed of the ultrasonic waves in air from your measured values of λ and f. How well does this agree with the value measured at audible frequencies?

Questions

1.   Using the known values $R = 8.31$ joule.mole^{-1}.$^{\circ}$K, $\gamma = 1.40$, and $M = 28.8 \times 10^{-3}$ kg for air, calculate the velocity of sound in air at 0°C. How well does this predicted value agree with your value determined from this experiment?

2.   What are the shortest and longest wavelengths of audible sound in air at 0°C?

3.   It is possible to produce ultrasonic waves with frequencies as high as 6×10^8 Hz. Calculate the wavelength of such a sound wave and compare its value with those of visible light, which range from 4×10^{-5} cm to 7×10^{-5} cm.

Name: _____   Partner(s): _____

_____

DATA TABLES

Room Temperature: T = _____ °C   (=_____K)

Method 1

Resonance Frequencies

f Hz	x_i cm	x_f cm	m	λ m	v m/s
				Average $\overline{v}$ =	

Method 2

AFO frequency, f = _____ khz

Values of 10λ

Trial #	Detector Positions (cm)		d (= 10λ)
	Initial	Final	(m)
1			
2			
3			
4			
5			
Mean Value $\overline{d}$ = m; $\therefore$ λ (= $\overline{d}$/10) = m			

Signature of Instructor: _____

Electric and Potential Fields

17

*The electric and potential fields set up by various charged bodies
will be examined, together with the effects produced on the fields
by the presence of a conductor and insulator.*

Introduction

If a small positive test charge (q_0) is placed in an electric field, it will experience a force $\vec{F}$ due to presence of the field. We define the *electric field*, $\vec{E}$, at the test charge location as:

$$\vec{E} = \frac{\vec{F}}{q_0} \qquad 1)$$

This equation provides us with a unit for measuring electric field strengths which, in the SI system, is the newton/coulomb. Like the force, $\vec{E}$ is a vector quantity and its direction is the same as the direction of the electrostatic force $\vec{F}$ acting on the test charge. If the electric field is set up by a positively charged object, then it points in the direction *away* from that object (i.e. the direction in which the positive test charge would move if free to do so under the influence of $\vec{F}$). If the field is due to a negatively charged object, then it points *toward* that object.

As an aid to visualizing the electric field, it is convenient to draw *electric field lines* (or *lines of force*). The electric field $\vec{E}$ at any point in space is then tangential to the (imaginary) field line through that point. There is, of course, an infinite number of points in space and we can draw only a few representative lines to describe the electric field.

The field set up by a charged body may be described not only by a vector electric field $\vec{E}$ but also by a scalar potential field V. The two fields are closely related. Suppose the test charge q_0 undergoes a small displacement $d\vec{s}$ under the influence of the force $\vec{F}$. The work done on the test charge by this force is then $\vec{F}.d\vec{s}$. The electrostatic force $\vec{F}$ is a conservative force. There must, therefore, be a potential energy function U associated with it, in which case the work done is also equal to the *decrease* in potential energy of the test charge, dU, i.e.

$$dU = -\vec{F}.d\vec{s} \qquad 2)$$

Note that only the change in potential energy is defined in this equation, not its absolute value.

Equation 2) can be written in terms of the electric field $\vec{E}$, i.e.

$$dU = -q_0\vec{E}.d\vec{s} \qquad 3)$$

Just as we defined the electric force as the electrostatic force per unit charge (eqn. 1), we may define a new quantity - the *electric potential difference*, dV - as the change in potential energy per unit charge, i.e.

$$dV = \frac{dU}{q_0} \qquad 4)$$

In SI units the potential difference is called the volt (v), which is equal to 1 joule/coulomb. Substitution in eqn. 3) now leads to the relationship:

$$dV = -\vec{E}.d\vec{s} \qquad 5)$$

This equation defines the change (dV) in a quantity V called the *electric potential*. Although it is only the *difference* in electric potential which has significance, it is nevertheless common practice to somewhat arbitrarily choose V to be zero at some convenient reference point and to measure the electric potential at all other points relative to this reference. When dealing with electrical circuitry, for example, it is usual to assign zero electric potential to the earth and to measure the potential at all other points relative to "ground". As in the case of potential energy, the electric potential V is a scalar quantity, and eqn. 5) shows the close relationship between V and the electric field $\vec{E}$.

A surface over which the electric potential is constant is called an *equipotential surface*. In this experiment we shall confine all measurements to a plane, in which case the locus of points having the same potential forms an *equipotential line*. A set of equipotential lines plotted in the vicinity of the charges may be taken to represent the potential field of the charges.

Suppose we move the test charge through a displacement $d\vec{s}$ at an angle θ to the direction of the electric field $\vec{E}$. The work done by the electrostatic force is $\vec{F}.d\vec{s}$ $(= F\ ds\ \cos\theta)$. Now if the displacement $d\vec{s}$ occurs along an equipotential line (or surface) then no work is done since there is no change in potential energy (dV = dU = 0). This means that $F\ ds\ \cos\theta = 0$, (i.e., θ=90°), so *the electrostatic force (and therefore the electric field $\vec{E}$) must always be perpendicular to an equipotential line or surface.

From eqn. 5), $dV = -E\ ds\ \cos\theta$ so the change in electric potential is a maximum when θ = 0°, i.e. when $d\vec{s}$ is parallel (or antiparallel) to $\vec{E}$. We therefore have:

$$E = -\frac{dV}{ds}, \quad d\vec{s}\|\vec{E} \qquad 6)$$

The electric field must, therefore, always point in the direction in which the electric potential has its *maximum* decrease[1]. We shall make use of this relationship between $\vec{E}$ and V expressed in

---

[1] A vector which always points in the direction in which a scalar has its maximum change, and whose magnitude is equal to the rate of change of that scalar function with respect to displacement in that direction, is called the **gradient** of the function. In the present case, the electric field E is the negative gradient of the potential V, and may be referred to as the potential gradient.

eqn.6) when mapping the electric field lines in the present experiment. Equation 6) also provides us with an alternative unit for measuring electric field strengths which, in SI units, may be expressed as volts/meter.

Although with proper instrumentation it is possible to measure the electric and potential fields between charges separated by air or vacuum, there are difficulties associated with this (for example, stray AC fields become a nuisance). These difficulties can largely be overcome by using a slightly conductive medium between the charges instead of air or vacuum. In this experiment we use weakly conductive paper on which metal conductors are attached. (This, of course, limits our study of fields to two dimensions.) The two outermost conductors are connected to the output terminals of a voltage power supply and serve as electrodes having charges of opposite sign. The electric field and electric potential will be measured in the region between these two electrodes. Also located in this region is a "floating" metal conductor to determine its influence on the two fields. The general arrangement for producing the fields is shown below.

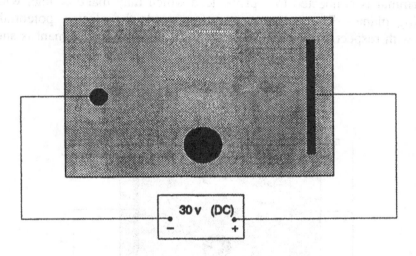

Figure 1:   *Field mapping circuit (without meter). The black areas are conductors, the two outer ones being charged. The white area is a cutout representing an insulator.*

Procedure

Mapping Potential Fields

i)   Mount the conductive sheet on the corkboard with the metal conductors attached. Connect the outer two conductors (the electrodes) across the power supply. This can be done by attaching connecting leads from the power supply to screws in the conductors using alligator clips.

ii)   Connect the ground terminal of the voltmeter to one of the electrodes. The other meter input terminal is connected to a probe lead which may make contact with any point in the conducting plane. The voltmeter therefore reads the electric potential at the probe tip location with respect to the first electrode. The general arrangement is shown in Fig. 2.

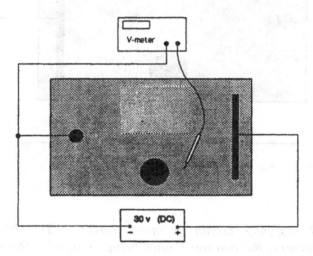

Figure 2: Electric circuit for mapping equipotential lines.

iii)   Turn on the power supply and adjust the output to 30 volts. Allow the probe tip to make contact with the conducting paper at a point near the first electrode. Note the voltmeter reading and make a small indentation in the paper at that point. Now move the probe to a new position where the voltmeter reads the same value as before and mark this new position on the paper. Continue this procedure to the edges of the paper. Since all measured points have the same electric potential, then a line drawn through them will correspond to an equipotential line. Draw a smooth line through the points and record at the edge of the paper the value of the voltage for this particular equipotential line.

iv)   Following this procedure, measure as many equipotential lines as necessary to provide a complete description of the potential field over the area of the conducting plane. Be especially careful in exploring the region near the floating conductor. Examine also the potential *inside* the conductor.

What effects does the conductor have on the potential field? What happens to the electric potential inside the conductor?

Mapping Electric Fields

As previously noted, the electric field at any point in space lies in the direction in which the rate of change of potential with displacement is a maximum. In any other direction, only a component of the electric field is experienced; in particular, in the direction along the equipotential line through the point this component goes to zero.

To measure electric field lines, either a small insulating rod or a rubber stopper, 1 cm radius, is supplied with a metal pin through its axis.

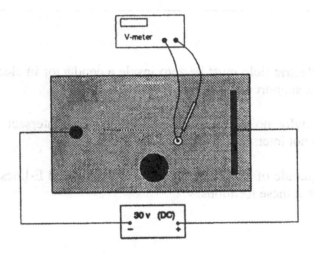

Figure 3. Circuit for mapping electric field lines.

v)   Pin the insulator rod to the conducting sheet near one of the electrodes and connect the ground terminal of the voltmeter to its centerpin (Fig. 3). Move the meter probe around the circumference of the rod and observe the meter readings. The meter reads the potential difference between points 1 cm apart at the rod. The electric field lies in the direction in which this potential difference is a maximum. Mark this corresponding position of the probe on the sheet and move the insulator rod to this new position. Repeat the procedure to determine the new position of the probe corresponding to maximum potential difference. Continue until the last data point ends either on the other electrode or on the conductor. Draw a *smooth* line through these data points. This represents an electric field line for this particular region between the two electrodes. Do your results agree with the expected behaviour that the electric field and equipotential lines are perpendicular to one another?

vi)   Now move the insulator rod *inside* the floating conductor and examine the electric field there. What happens to the electric field inside the conductor?

vii)   For the remaining conducting plane we shall make use of the fact that the electric field at any point is perpendicular to the equipotential line through that point. Starting on an equipotential line near one of the electrodes, draw a line across the plane such that it is perpendicular to all equipotential lines which it crosses. (The electric field line can end either on the other electrode or on the conductor.) Proceed in this manner with other lines until a sufficiently detailed description is had of the electric field over the entire area of the conducting plane. Pay particular attention to the region near the conductor.

How is the electric field affected by the presence of the floating conductor?

Questions

1.   Explain why the electric field must be zero inside a conductor in electrostatic equilibrium. Do your measurements support this statement?

2.   Explain carefully why no two electric field lines can intersect one another. Why can equipotential lines not intersect one another?

3.   Calculate the magnitude of E at three locations along plotted E-lines. Show also the direction of the electric field at these locations.

Capacitors and RC Decay

18

The laws governing the rate of charging and discharging of a capacitor will be studied and applied to the measurement of capacitance.

Introduction

A capacitor is essentially a charge storing device. If a charge $+Q$ is added to one plate of a capacitor and a charge $-Q$ to the other, the resulting potential difference V between the plates is proportional to Q. This relationship may be expressed in the form:

$$Q = CV \qquad\qquad 1)$$

where C is called the *capacitance* of the capacitor. In SI units (Q in coulombs, V in volts) the unit of capacitance is the farad (abbreviated F). However, the farad is an extremely large unit of capacitance and most commonly used capacitors are measured in microfarads ($1\,\mu F = 10^{-6}F$) or even picofarads ($1pF = 10^{-12}F$).

A. Parallel and Series Capacitors

If two capacitors with capacitance values C_1 and C_2 are connected in parallel, as shown in Fig. 1, the combined capacitance C_p of this parallel combination is given by:

$$C_p = C_1 + C_2 \qquad\qquad 2)$$

If C_1 and C_2 are instead connected in series (Fig. 2), the combined capacitance C_s of this series combination is given by the expression:

$$\frac{1}{C_s} = \frac{1}{C_1} + \frac{1}{C_2}$$

or
$$C_s = \frac{C_1 C_2}{C_1 + C_2} \qquad\qquad 3)$$

We shall test these relations for parallel and series connection of capacitors, using the properties of resistance/capacitance circuits to measure capacitance.

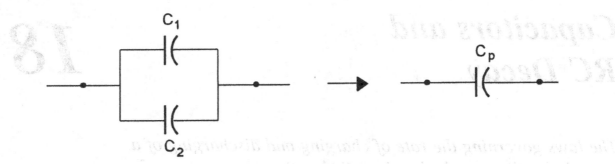

Figure 1: Capacitors connected in parallel.

Fiqure 2: Capacitors connected in series.

B. The RC Circuit

Shown in Fig. 3 are a capacitor and resistor connected in a circuit containing also a DC voltage source (output voltage V_o), a switch (S) and voltmeter (V).

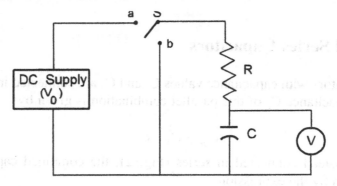

Figure 3: Resistance-Capacitance Circuit

We shall examine the voltage which is developed across the capacitor when the switch is closed in the circuit, first at terminal "a" and then at terminal "b".

Capacitor Charging

When the switch is connected to terminal "a", the resistor and capacitor are connected to the DC voltage supply and a current i flows in the circuit which serves to charge the capacitor. If we denote the voltages across the resistor and capacitor by V_r and V_c, respectively, then

$$V_o = V_r + V_c$$

The charge builds up on the capacitor at a rate which is governed by an exponential law and is given by:

$$Q = CV_o (1-e^{-t/RC})$$

where e (=2.718..) is the base of natural logarithms. This also leads directly to an expression for the voltage V_c across the capacitor as a function of time, since

$$V_c = Q/C = V_o(1-e^{-t/RC}) \qquad\qquad 4)$$

A plot of either Q or V_c against time will have the same general shape, as shown in Fig. 4 for the voltage.

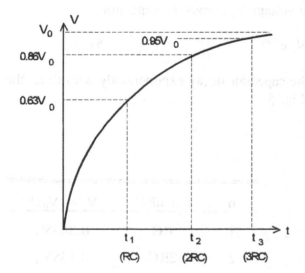

n	t = nRC	$V_c = V_0(1-e^{-n})$
1	RC	$0.623V_0$
2	2RC	$0.865V_0$
3	3RC	$0.950V_0$
4	4RC	$0.982V_0$

Figure 4: Capacitor charging

Since the exponent (-t/RC) in the equations above must be dimensionless, the product RC must have the dimension of time and is referred to as the *time constant* of the circuit. If R is measured in ohms and C in farads, then the product RC is in units of seconds.

If we set the time t equal to integer multiples of RC, i.e. if:

$$t = nRC, \text{ where } n = 1, 2, 3,.....\text{etc,}$$

then:

$$V_c = V_o(1-e^{-n})$$

Values of the voltage V_c for n = 1,2,3, and 4 are given in the table alongside Fig. 4. We see that after a time interval t_1 = RC after closing the switch, the voltage on the capacitor has risen to 63% of the maximum value of V_o; after the interval t_2 = 2RC it is 86% of V_o, and so on. By measuring the times taken to reach these values, the product RC can be determined; and if the circuit resistance is known, the capacitance C can be found.

Capacitor Discharging

Suppose that, after the capacitor has been fully charged to a voltage $V_c = V_o$, the switch is connected to terminal "b" in the circuit of Fig. 3. With the voltage supply now isolated in the circuit, and with the resistor and capacitor alone in the loop, the loop theorem yields the relationship:

$$V_r + V_c = 0$$

The charge on the capacitor now leaks through the resistor at a rate given by:

$$Q = CV_o \, e^{-t/RC}$$

As before, we may write this equation in terms of the voltage V_c across the capacitor,

$$V_c = Q/C = V_o \, e^{-t/RC} \qquad\qquad 5)$$

This equation shows that the charge and voltage on the capacitor decay exponentially with time, the time-dependence having the general shape shown in Fig. 5.

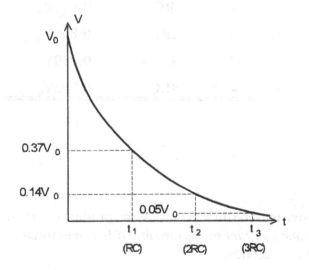

n	t = nRC	$V_c = V_0 e^{-n}$
1	RC	$0.368V_0$
2	2RC	$0.135V_0$
3	3RC	$0.050V_0$
4	4RC	$0.018V_0$

Figure 5: *Capacitor discharging*

The rate of decay of the voltage (or charge) on the capacitor is again determined by the time constant RC of the circuit, and if as before we choose time intervals which are integer multiples n of RC (t = nRC), we may write:

$$V_c = V_o\, e^{-n}$$

Values of V_c for n = 1, 2, 3 and 4 are given in the table alongside Fig. 5. We see that after a time interval t_1 = RC after closing the switch to terminal "b", the voltage on the capacitor has dropped to 36.8% of its initial value V_o; after an interval t_2 = 2RC it is just 13.5% of V_o, and so on. Equation 12) shows that the rate of discharge decreases as the voltage decreases, and theoretically V_c never reaches zero. In practice, however, V_c becomes negligibly small after a period equal to a few time constants.

By choosing suitable values for resistance and capacitance, circuits may be designed having a wide range of different time constants. For example, with R = 5 MΩ and C = 10 μF, the time constant t_1 = RC = $(5 \times 10^6)(10 \times 10^{-6})$ = 50 sec; if R = 100 Ω and C = 0.1 μF, then t_1 = $(100)(0.1 \times 10^{-6})$ = 10×10^{-6} sec., or 10μ sec.

Note that the time constant of the circuit (t_1 = RC) is the time necessary for the voltage (or charge) to decay to 1/e (= 0.368) of its original value V_0. A related quantity is the *half-life*, $t_{1/2}$, which is the time required for the voltage (charge) to decrease to just one-half the original value. This is given by:

$$\frac{V_c}{V_0} = \frac{1}{2} = e^{-t_{1/2}/RC}$$

or, $$t_{1/2} = RC\, \ell n 2 = 0.693\, RC \qquad\qquad 6)$$

The concept of half-life is widely used in describing the rate of radioactive decay, which also follows the exponential law of decay.

C. Time Constants

To measure the change in voltage on the capacitor as a function of time a voltmeter must be placed across it, as shown in Fig. 3. The voltmeter-capacitor circuit therefore forms a closed loop which can, in principle, also carry a current unless the resistance in this loop is infinitely great. In the previous discussion it has been assumed that the voltmeter is an ideal one having an infinite resistance. In this case the capacitor can only be charged or discharged through the loop containing the resistor R in Fig. 3. In practice, however, a voltmeter does have finite (though usually very large) internal resistance value and the circuit resistance which determines the rate of charging or discharging of the capacitor is a combination of the resistance R *and* the voltmeter resistance. In Fig. 6 is shown a more realistic circuit, in which the voltmeter is represented by the dashed lines surrounding the meter display (V) and its internal resistance R_m.

In this experiment we shall be able to dispense with the use of an external resistance for most measurements and use just the internal resistance of the voltmeter to provide the circuit resistance. The voltmeter will therefore serve both as a means of measuring the voltage across the capacitor and as a parallel resistor through which the capacitor discharges.

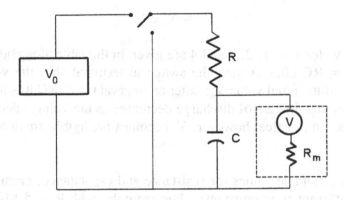

Figure 6: *RC circuit including also the internal resistance of the voltmeter.*

Procedure

Time constants will be measured for several different RC circuits. From these and the known circuit resistances, values of the circuit capacitances will be determined. In the first part of the experiment we shall examine RC circuits having relatively long time constants (10-200 secs.) which can be measured using conventional timers. The combination laws for capacitors connected in parallel and in series will also be tested. In the second part, we shall study circuits having much shorter time constants (10-200 μsec.). In this case conventional timers and voltmeters are inadequate and we shall require instead, a cathode ray oscilloscope (CRO) for measuring such small time constants.

Part A. Long Time Constants

The voltmeter used in this part has an internal resistance of several megohms, the precise value to be determined by measurement. Two capacitors will be used, first separately and then in combination in the circuit. The basic circuit is shown in Figure 7, in which the voltmeter alone provides the circuit resistance.

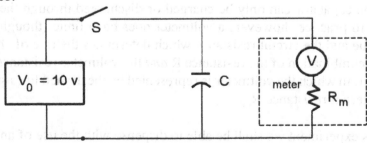

Figure 7: *RC circuit for studying capacitor discharge.*

Note that without the external resistor R in the circuit the full charging voltage V_o is applied directly to the plates of the capacitor as soon as the switch is closed, the capacitor thus becoming fully charged ($Q_o = CV_o$) without delay. (This is equivalent to setting $R = 0$ in eqns. 4) and 5). The exponential rise with time of the capacitor voltage cannot, therefore, be studied using this circuit. When the switch is opened, however, the capacitor will discharge exponentially with time through the voltmeter. The time constant R_mC can be measured and if R_m is known the value of the circuit capacitance C can be determined.

Measurement of R_m

i)   Set up the circuit of Fig. 7, using the larger of the two capacitors (C_1) for C. Close the switch and adjust the output voltage of the power supply to $V_o = 10.0$ volts, as measured by the meter. Now open the switch and simultaneously start the timer. Measure the time taken for the capacitor voltage to drop to 3.68v, i.e., to 36.8% of its initial value. This is equal to the time constant of the circuit (see Fig. 5), and if we denote this by t', then

$$t' = R_mC_1 \qquad\qquad 7)$$

Repeat this for at least three independent measurements of t', and determine the average value.

ii)   Now connect an external resistor, $R_x = 10$ MΩ (1% precision value) in parallel with the capacitor and meter, as shown in Fig. 8. Repeat procedure (i) to measure the time constant t'' corresponding to this new circuit resistance. The total resistance in this circuit is given by the parallel combination of R_m and R_x, i.e.,

$$R = \frac{R_xR_m}{R_x + R_m}$$

and $\qquad\qquad t'' = \dfrac{R_xR_m}{R_x + R_m}C_1 = \dfrac{R_x}{R_x + R_m}\, t'$

where the quantity R_mC_1 has been replaced by t'. Rearranging this equation leads to the result:

$$R_m = \frac{t' - t''}{t''}\, R_x$$

from which R_m can be determined. Be sure to remove the external resistor R_x from the circuit after this measurement.

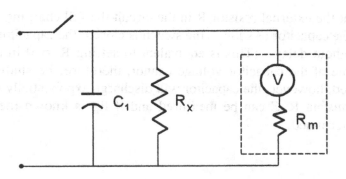

Figure 8: Measurement of R_m

Measurement of Capacitance

The circuit of Fig. 7 will be used with different circuit capacitances.

iii)   Using the now known value R_m for the meter resistance and the measured time constant t', calculate the value of the capacitance C_1 for the larger capacitor (equation 7).

iv)   Replace the larger capacitor in the circuit with the smaller capacitor C_2, and close the switch to charge it to the voltage V_o. If necessary adjust the power supply again to $V_o = 10.0v$. Open the switch and measure the time for the capacitor voltage to drop to 3.68v. Repeat for three measurements and use the average value to compute the capacitance C_2.

v)   Now connect both capacitors C_1 and C_2 in series, with the voltmeter across both of them (Fig. 9a). The circuit capacitance is now C_s which can be measured following the procedure in step (iv).

vi)   Finally, repeat step (iv) with both capacitors connected in parallel in the circuit (Fig. 9b). Determine the combined capacitance C_p.

vii)   From the measured values of C_1 and C_2, calculate (eqns. 2 and 3) the *predicted* combined capacitances when connected in series (C_s) and in parallel (C_p). How well do these agree with the *measured* values of (C_s) and (C_p) from (v) and (vi)?

(a)   (b)

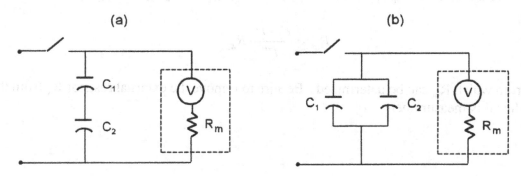

Figure 9: Series (a) and parallel (b) connected capacitors.

Exponential Decay

In the previous sections we assumed properties of the exponential decay law to extract values of the circuit capacitance. To study this law in more detail we shall need to plot the capacitance voltage V_c -vs- time.

viii)   Set up the circuit of Fig. 7 using only the *larger* capacitor C_1. Close the switch and charge the capacitor to V_o = 10.0v. Open the switch and record values of the capacitor voltage at 10 second intervals until the voltage has dropped to 0.3v. These measurements therefore span a time interval slightly in excess of three time constants (i.e., $3R_mC_1$).

Plot a graph of V_c -vs.- time. Obtain three separate determinations of the time constant R_mC_1, corresponding (see Fig. 5) to V_c = 3.68v ($t_1 = R_mC_1$), V_c = 1.35v ($t_2 = 2R_mC_1$), and V_c = 0.50v ($t_3 = 3R_mC_1$). From the average of the time constants and knowing R_m, calculate again the capacitance C_1.

The voltage-time relationship expressed in the equation

$$V_c = V_0 e^{-t/R_mC_1}$$

may be represented by a linear plot if we take natural logarithms of both sides of the equation, i.e.,

$$\ln V_c = \ln V_0 - \frac{t}{R_mC_1}$$

A plot of $\log_e V_c$ -vs.- time is seen to be a straight line with a slope equal to $-1/R_mC_1$ and whose intercept at t = 0 is $\log_e V_o$. Make a plot of $\log_e V_c$ -vs.- time and from its slope determine the capacitance C_1. How well does this value compare with previous measurements?

Part B. Short Time Constants

To measure short time constants, say < 1 ms (1 ms = 1 millisec = 1 x 10^{-3} s), it is necessary to use a voltmeter capable of responding to very rapid changes in voltage level, a timer capable of measuring down to 1μs, and a fast-acting switch which can be synchronized with the timer. A cathode ray oscilloscope can serve both as a voltmeter and timer for such measurements. An audio-frequency oscillator (AFO) capable of generating a square-wave voltage output can also be used to combine the functions of both the fast-acting switch and the power supply. The output voltage of frequency f = 1/T from such a square wave generator is depicted in fig. 10(a). If such a voltage is applied to a capacitor-resistor pair then the capacitor will alternately charge and discharge through the resistor, its voltage varying with time according to fig. 10(b). (It is assumed in this figure that the period of the generated waveform T is approximately equal to 8RC, so that the capacitor becomes nearly fully charged or discharged during successive half-periods.) If the CRO is connected across the capacitor, the capacitor voltage of Figure 10(b) can be displayed on the oscilloscope. The sweep frequency of the CRO may be adjusted so that just one full period T of the AFO output is displayed. If the time-axis is calibrated, then the time constant of the circuit can be measured.

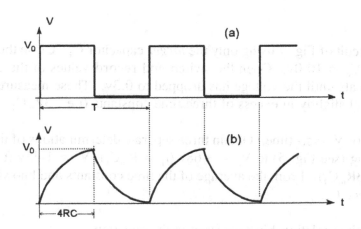

Figure 10:   *Shown in (a) is a AFO square wave voltage applied to a capacitor-resistor pair, and in (b) the resulting capacitor voltage as a function of time. It is assumed that $T \approx 8\ RC$.*

The circuit is shown in Fig. 11. The AFO square wave generator has an internal resistance $R_g = 600\Omega$. This can therefore provide the circuit resistance through which the capacitor charges and discharges, an external resistor being unnecessary. The time constant of the circuit is, therefore, $R_g C$.

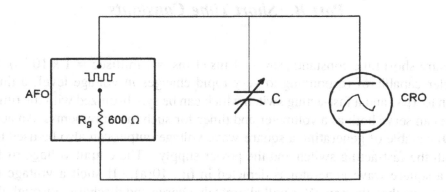

Figure 11: *Circuit for measuring time constant, $(T = R_g C)$*

ix)   Set up the circuit of Fig. 11 with C ~ 0.22µF. The CRO and AFO should have the initial settings shown in the following table. Make any necessary adjustments to the CRO controls to obtain a stable display of the charge/discharge curves within the axis limits on the screen.

	CRO	AFO
Y-Amplifier:	1v/Div.	Square Wave Output
	AC coupled	1 kHz frequency
		Max. Output
Time Base:	Auto Trig.	
	100µs/Div.	
	(calibrated)	

x)   Measure the half-life $t_{1/2}$ for both the charging cycle and the discharging cycle, and from the average value compute the time constant (eqn. 6). How well does this agree with the time constant calculated from the known values of R_g and C?

An important property of RC circuits is their ability to change the shape of an input voltage signal. This is clearly demonstrated in the previous step, in which the output voltage from the capacitor is seen to bear little resemblance in shape to the input square waveform from the AFO. This property of shaping waveforms is widely used in electronics. An important parameter which determines the shape of the output voltage from the capacitor is the ratio of the period T of the input signal to the time constant of the circuit.

xii)   To examine the effect of T on the shape of the output waveform, slowly increase the frequency of the AFO output from 1 kHz to 20 kHz. Observe the change in the output waveform shape, recording the waveforms displayed on the CRO at frequencies of 2, 5, 10 and 20 kHz. At each of these frequencies adjust the CRO sweep frequency so that only one period T is displayed on the screen and increase the Y-amplification as needed for the waveform to fill the screen.

How does the shape of the output voltage change as the period T becomes small compared with the time constant R_gC. Explain this behaviour.

Questions

1.   An RC circuit has a resistance of 20 MΩ and a time constant of 100 sec. If the capacitor is charged to a voltage of 10v, what is the charge in coulombs on its plates?

2.   A charged 1μF capacitor is connected in parallel with a 1MΩ resistor. How long after the connection is made will the capacitor voltage drop to a) 50%, b) 10%, and c) 2% of its initial value?

3.   How many 1μF capacitors would need to be connected in parallel in order to store a charge of 1 coulomb with a potential of 200 volts across the capacitors?

Name: _____   Partner(s): _____

_____

TABLE I: *Measurement of Capacitance*

t' - Capacitor C_1 (see eqn. 7 and fig. 7)
t'' - Capacitor C_1 and R_x (see fig. 8)
t_2 - Capacitor C_2
t_s - Capacitors C_1 and C_2 in series
t_p - Capacitors C_1 and C_2 in parallel *Note:* $C_1 > C_2$

Trial	t' (s)	t'' (s)	t_2 (s)	t_s (s)	t_p (s)
1					
2					
3					
Average					

$R_m = $ _____ Ω

$C_1 = $ _____ μF ; $C_2 = $ _____ μF ; $C_S = $ _____ μF ; $C_P = $ _____ μF

TABLE II: *measurement of exponential RC decay (*with C_1)

t (sec)	V (volts)	t (sec)	V (volts)	t (sec)	V (volts)
0	10.0				

Signature of Instructor: _____

Name: _____   Partner(s) _____

TABLE A. Measurement of Capacitance

1. — Capacitor C_1 (see eqn 7 and fig. 5)
2. — Capacitor C_2 and P_3 (see fig. X)
3. — Capacitor C_3
4. — Capacitors C_1, C_2 and C_3 in series
5. — Capacitors C_1 and C_2 in parallel, Note: $C_p = C_q$

Trial	t (s)	V (V)	t (s)	q (μC)	C (F)
1					
2					
3					
Average					

$R_s =$ _____ Ω

$C_1 =$ _____ μF $C_2 =$ _____ μF $C_3 =$ _____ μF $C_4 =$ _____ μF

TABLE B. measurement of exponential AC decay (volts.)

t (sec)	V (volts)	t (sec)	V (volts)	t (sec)	V (volts)
0	0.00				

Signature of Instructor _____

Charged Particle Motion in Magnetic Fields   *19*

The charge-to-mass ratio (e/m) for the electron will be determined from measurements of the trajectory of electrons in a magnetic field.

Introduction

In his investigations of cathode rays, J.J. Thomson showed conclusively that they consisted of negatively charged particles which he associated with electrons. In addition, by measuring the deflection of the rays in magnetic and electric fields, Thomson made the first determination of the ratio of the charge of the electron to its mass, e/m. Using a value for "e" deduced from other studies he was then able to show that its mass must be some 2000 times less than that of the lightest atom, hydrogen.

In this experiment we shall measure the charge-to-mass ratio (e/m) of the electron using a magnetic deflection technique and a specially designed electron vacuum tube. Electrons are ejected by thermionic emission from a cathode which is indirectly heated by a hot wire filament (see Fig. 1). A potential difference V applied between the anode and cathode of the electron gun causes the electrons to accelerate toward the anode, thus acquiring an amount of kinetic energy given by:

$$\frac{1}{2}mv^2 = eV \quad \text{...} \quad 1)$$

After acceleration, the electron beam emerges through a small aperture into the tube region beyond the anode. (The grid electrode serves to focus the beam through this aperture.) To provide a visible trace of the electron trajectory in the glass tube, the tube is evacuated during its manufacture and then filled with a small amount of an inert gas to a pressure of about 10^{-2} torr. When the electrons collide with the gas atoms some of the atoms become ionized. As the ions quickly recombine with other stray electrons, light is emitted having wavelengths characteristic of the inert gas atom. Since recombination and emission occur very near the point where initial ionization takes place, the path of the electrons is made clearly visible as they travel through the gas.

If a magnetic field B exists within the tube then this will exert a force on the moving electrons. If θ is the angle between the direction of the electron's velocity vector and the magnetic field direction, then the magnitude of the force is given by the Lorentz relation:

$$|F| = Bev \sin\theta \quad \text{...} \quad 2)$$

This force will cause the electrons to be deflected and in general to follow the path of an open spiral. If, however, the magnetic field is aligned so as to be perpendicular to the direction of motion of the electrons (i.e., θ = 90°) then the force exerted on them will also be perpendicular to their velocity vector and so will not affect its magnitude. The magnetic force thus acts as a centripetal force (of magnitude mv²/r) causing the electrons to move in a circular orbit of radius r which can be obtained from the equation:

$$Bev = \frac{mv^2}{r} \qquad \text{3)}$$

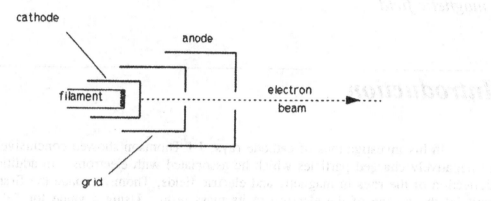

Figure 1: *Electrode configuration inside the electron tube.*

Eliminating v between eqns. 1) and 3) we arrive at the relation:

$$\frac{e}{m} = \frac{2V}{B^2 r^2} \qquad \text{4)}$$

All quantities on the right of this equation can be measured to give a value of e/m for the electron. If V is measured in volts, B in teslas and r in meters, then the charge-to-mass ratio is in coulombs/kg.

In this experiment, the magnetic field B is provided by a pair of Helmholtz coils. This is a special arrangement of two identical, co-axial coils which carry equal electric currents and are separated by a distance equal to their radius. This geometry produces a magnetic field in the region midway between the two coils (where the electron tube is located) which is very nearly uniform, a necessary requirement to ensure that the electrons experience a constant force over their trajectory. The value of the magnetic field along the axis of the coils and at the midpoint is given by:

$$B = \left(\frac{8}{\sqrt{125}}\right)\frac{\mu_0 NI}{R} \qquad \text{5)}$$

in which $\mu_0 = 4\pi \times 10^{-7}$ weber/amp.-meter (the permeability of free space), N is the number of turns in each coil, I is the current in the coils and R is the coil radius. Note that by adjusting the current I the magnetic field strength can be changed. The unit of B is the tesla if I is in amperes and R in meters. If we substitute this expression for B into eqn. 4) we obtain:

$$\frac{e}{m} = C\frac{V}{(Ir)^2} \quad\text{...} \quad 6)$$

$$\text{where} \quad C = \frac{125}{32}\left(\frac{R}{\mu_0 N}\right)^2 \quad\text{...} \quad 7)$$

For a given set of Helmholtz coils C is a constant. According to eqn. 6), therefore, the only adjustable experimental parameters in the measurement of e/m are the accelerating voltage V, the electron trajectory radius r, and the coil current I.

Procedure

i)   Measure and record the mean diameter of either coil (D) and the number of turns per coil (N) indicated on the base of the Helmholtz coil assembly. Calculate the constant C in eqn.7), using the mean radius R of the coils.

ii)   Complete the circuit shown in Fig. 2. Two power supplies are needed, one to provide current to the Helmholtz coils and one to power the electron gun. Typical requirements are:

> Helmholtz coils :   1 - 3 amp,   DC
> Filament current: 6.3 volts,   AC
> Anode voltage :   150 - 300v, DC

The electron tube and coils are mounted on a terminal chassis. When connecting the power supplies and meters to this chassis be careful to observe the polarities indicated on the front panel. Turn the chassis current adjust control for the coils to maximum and set the front panel switch to "e/m" position. No connections should be made to the terminals labelled "Deflect Plates". Turn all voltage and current controls on the power supplies to zero.

iii)   Turn on the power supply for the electron tube. Allow about two minutes for the filament to heat up and then increase the anode voltage to about 200v. A straight beam should now be observed from the electron gun to the glass wall of the tube opposite the anode.

iv)   Now turn on the current supply for the coils and slowly increase the current. Observe the bending of the electron trajectory which should eventually become a closed full circle. If necessary, adjust the focus control on the front panel to obtain a well defined beam.

v)   As noted previously, the general orbital path of a charged particle in a magnetic field is an open spiral. Observe this by rotating the electron tube so that the angle which the velocity of the electrons makes with the magnetic field direction varies between 0° and

90°. Note that the circular orbit (which is merely a closed spiral) occurs when the velocity and magnetic field vectors are perpendicular to one another. Examine the beam trajectory for several values of accelerating voltage, coil current and tube orientation.

vi)   Now rotate the tube to obtain a closed circular orbit. Adjust the magnetic field strength (coil current I) and the accelerating voltage (V) to give a large circular trajectory which reaches almost to the glass wall. Adjust the height of the mirror scale at the back of the tube so that its center coincides with that of the trajectory, as judged by eye.

The mirrored scale has a center zero and is graduated in 1-mm intervals on either side of zero. The trajectory radius can, therefore, be measured both to the left (r_1) and to the right (r_2) of zero and averaged (be sure to avoid uncertainties due to parallax). Record these values and also the corresponding values of V and I (Table I). Try additional readings using different values of V and I but keeping the radius at about the same value.

vii)   Repeat this procedure for different values of the trajectory radius. Be sure to adjust the mirror scale each time the radius is changed.

viii) For each set of data calculate e/m and compute the average of their values. How well does this average compare with the accepted value of 1.76×10^{11} coul./kg ?

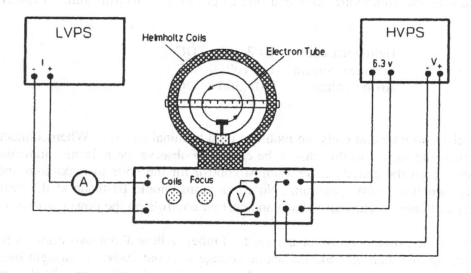

Figure 2: Schematic arrangement for e/m measurement.

Extended Analysis

The measured e/m values from the entire class may be gathered on a sheet by each group entering their values by hand, the sheet reproduced by your instructor, and each student obtaining a copy so as to subject a statistically significant number of measurements to statistical analysis. This analysis is explained on page III-4 in the section, *B. Random Errors and the Normal (Gaussian) Distribution.*

The steps in this analysis procedure are as follows:

1) Generate a table by hand of all the values from smallest to largest. Have a second column for calculating deviations from the mean.

2) Choose a bin width such that one has at least 15 measurements in the central bin.

3) Generate a table of frequency distribution of e/m values (e.g. *Table III-2*).

4) Graph histogram of this frequency distribution. Use straight edge here. (e.g. *Figure 1*).

5) The distribution should appear Gaussian (bell shaped) unless systematic errors dominate some of the values.

6) Calculate the mean e/m value (see page III-7). Here use some discretion as to which values might be considered outliers not following the bell shaped distribution. These outlier values should be excluded when calculating the mean.

7) Fill in the deviation from the mean column (see page III-8) in your table above.

8) Now calculate the root-mean-square (rms) deviation D (see page III-8) excluding deviations from the outliers.

9) Compare the mean value to the accepted value for e/m by calculating a percent difference.

10) Does your value fall within the mean value +/- D? One expects about a 2/3 probability (0.683) that this should be the case.

11) What decimal fraction of values actually fall within the mean value +/- D range? Here again exclude outliers from the analysis.

Questions

1.   Calculate the magnetic field in the electron tube corresponding to a) the smallest current, and b) the the largest current in the Helmholtz coils. How do these values compare in magnitude with the earth's magnetic field (approximately 5×10^{-5} tesla)?

2.   The accepted value of 1.76×10^{11} coul./kg for e/m corresponds only to electrons at rest. According to Einstein's special theory of relativity, however, the mass of a particle is not constant but depends on its velocity. If we denote its mass when at rest by m_0 and its mass when moving at velocity v by m, then:

$$m = \frac{m_0}{\sqrt{1 - v^2/c^2}} = \gamma m_0, \quad \text{where } \gamma = \frac{1}{\sqrt{1 - v^2/c^2}}$$

where c ($= 3 \times 10^8$ m/s) is the velocity of light and $m_0 = 9.1 \times 10^{-31}$ kg. The classical expression for the kinetic energy of a particle, K, (see eqn. 1) is also only valid at non-relativistic velocities and the true relativistic relationship is given by:

$$K = mc^2 - m_0 c^2 = m_0 c^2 (\gamma - 1) = eV$$

Solving for γ, $\gamma = 1 + \dfrac{eV}{m_0 c^2}$

Using e $= 1.602 \times 10^{-19}$C for the charge of the electron, calculate γ for the largest accelerating voltage used in this experiment and from this determine the velocity of the electrons. What percentage of the velocity of light is this? If the value 1.76×10^{11} coul./kg corresponds to e/m_0, what would be the accepted value of e/m at this velocity?

Name: _____   Partner(s):   _____

_____

Experimental Data and Results

$$\frac{e}{m} = C\frac{V}{(Ir)^2}; \qquad C = \frac{125}{32}\left(\frac{R}{\mu_0 N}\right)^2 \quad \text{where } \mu_0 = 4\pi.\ 10^{-7}\ W/amp.m$$

Number of turns/coil:	N =	
Outer coil diameter :	D_o =	m
Inner " " :	D_i =	m
Mean " " :	D =	m
∴ Mean coil radius :	R =	m
∴	C =	SI units

Table I: Electron Beam Trajectory Parameters

Data Set	V (volts)	I (amp)	r_1 (m)	r_2 (m)	∴ r (m)	e/m (coul/kg)
1						
2						
3						
4						
5						
6						
7						
8						
9						
10						
		∴ Mean Value (e/m) =				

Signature of Instructor: _____

Atomic Energy Levels: Balmer Series of Hydrogen   **20**

Using a grating spectroscope, the Balmer spectrum emitted by hydrogen will be examined together with the spectra from several other gaseous light sources.

Introduction

When the atoms of a gas are excited into any of the allowed energy levels above their ground state, they return to their ground state by releasing energy in the form of light. The wavelength of the emitted light depends on the energy differences between the initial and final states of the emitting atoms. Since only certain energy values are allowed for the atoms of each element, however, then only certain wavelengths are emitted, which are characteristic of the element. Such spectra are, therefore, referred to as **characteristic spectra**. If the light from a gas discharge tube is viewed through a spectroscope, a spectrum will be seen consisting of a series of colored images of the aperture of the spectrometer, with each one corresponding to one of the component wavelengths in the light source. Since the aperture is usually a vertical slit, the images appear as bright vertical lines and the name **line spectrum** is commonly used to describe the spectra.

The interpretation of line spectra in terms of the structure of the emitting atoms is now well understood and spectral measurements are commonly applied in the spectrochemical analysis of materials. In this experiment we shall use a grating spectrometer to study the visible line spectrum of hydrogen and to examine the spectra emitted by several other gas sources.

The Hydrogen Spectrum

The simplest atomic structure is that of the hydrogen atom, which comprises a single electron orbiting around a proton nucleus. Niels Bohr showed that the possible energy values for the hydrogen atom are given by the formula:

$$E_n = \frac{-13.6}{n^2} \ eV, \quad where \ n = 1, 2, 3...etc. \qquad 1)$$

The integer n is called the *principal quantum number*. The lowest energy level, or **ground state**, has an energy $E_1 = -13.6$ eV, corresponding to n = 1. (The electron-volt is a unit of energy whereby 1 eV = 1.6×10^{-19} J.) Higher energy levels correspond to larger principal quantum numbers and to different electron orbitals.

Suppose a hydrogen atom absorbs energy, e.g., as in a hydrogen discharge tube. Its electron is thereby raised to a higher energy orbital which we characterize by the principal quantum number n and energy E_n. The atom now quickly returns to its ground state energy (n = 1 level) either directly or by a succession of transitions between any intermediate states whose energies lie between E_n and E_1. For each transition a photon of light is emitted whose energy is equal to the difference in energy between the initial (i) and final (f) states. The energy of the photon determines the frequency, υ, of the light emitted and is given by $h\upsilon$, where h is Planck's constant. Thus, if the atom makes a transition from an initial state with energy E_{ni} and principal quantum number n_i, to a final state with energy E_{nf} and principal quantum number n_f, the energy of the emitted photon is given by:

$$h\nu = E_{n_i} - E_{n_f} = 13.6 \left(\frac{1}{n_f^2}\right) eV \qquad\qquad 2)$$

Since $c = \lambda\upsilon$, we can express this relationship in terms of the wavelength of the light emitted in this transition between energy levels, i.e.

$$\left(\frac{1}{\lambda_{f \to i}}\right) = R\left(\frac{1}{n_f^2} - \frac{1}{n_i^2}\right) \qquad\qquad 3)$$

In this equation, R (= 13.6 eV/hc) is a constant known as the **Rydberg constant**, whose value is 1.097×10^7 m^{-1}.

Equation 3) gives rise to several well known series of lines in the hydrogen spectrum. In each of these series all transitions occur to the same final energy level, so that each series can be characterized by the principal quantum number (n_f) corresponding to that final state, as indicated in Table I. These series are also customarily named after their discoverers, and of these only the Balmer series contains lines which occur in the visible region of the electromagnetic spectrum. These lines correspond to the first three transitions in the Balmer series and are designated by the symbols H_α, H_β, H_γ, respectively. Thus,

$$H_\alpha \text{ (red):} \qquad \left(\frac{1}{\lambda_\alpha}\right) = R\left(\frac{1}{2^2} - \frac{1}{3^2}\right)$$

$$H_\beta \text{ (blue):} \qquad \left(\frac{1}{\lambda_\beta}\right) = R\left(\frac{1}{2^2} - \frac{1}{4^2}\right)$$

$$H_\gamma \text{ (violet):} \qquad \left(\frac{1}{\lambda_\gamma}\right) = R\left(\frac{1}{2^2} - \frac{1}{5^2}\right)$$

The Rydberg constant can be determined from measurements of the wavelengths for these lines.

TABLE I: *The Hydrogen Series*

Series Name	Final Level (n_f)	Relationship	Initial Level (n_i)	Spectral Region
Lyman	1	$\left(\dfrac{1}{\lambda}\right) = R\left(\dfrac{1}{1^2} - \dfrac{1}{n_i^2}\right)$	$n_i = 2, 3, 4\ \ldots$	UV
Balmer	2	$\left(\dfrac{1}{\lambda}\right) = R\left(\dfrac{1}{2^2} - \dfrac{1}{n_i^2}\right)$	$n_i = 3, 4, 5\ \ldots$	UV - visible
Paschen	3	$\left(\dfrac{1}{\lambda}\right) = R\left(\dfrac{1}{3^2} - \dfrac{1}{n_i^2}\right)$	$n_i = 4, 5, 6\ \ldots$	IR
Bracket	4	$\left(\dfrac{1}{\lambda}\right) = R\left(\dfrac{1}{4^2} - \dfrac{1}{n_i^2}\right)$	$n_i = 5, 6, 7\ \ldots$	IR
Pfund	5	$\left(\dfrac{1}{\lambda}\right) = R\left(\dfrac{1}{5^2} - \dfrac{1}{n_i^2}\right)$	$n_i = 6, 7, 8\ \ldots$	Far IR

Grating Spectrometer

The grating spectrometer used for this study is shown schematically in Fig. 1. Details of its principle of operation can be found in Experiment 14. The spectrometer consists of a light-tight case having an adjustable (0 - 1 mm) slit at one end (S) and an eyepiece (E) at the other end. Light from a source (L) illuminates the slit and is incident on a transmission grating (G). The spectral lines characteristic of the source are observed as virtual images of the slit superimposed on a scale (AB), which is curved to eliminate parallax between the images and the scale. The scale readings are arbitrary and so must first be calibrated in terms of wavelength. This is best carried out using a light source whose line spectrum is very well known. The helium emission spectrum is particularly well suited for this purpose, since it possesses a number of prominent lines over the entire visible region. These are listed in Table II together with their relative intensities (strong-s, medium-m, weak-w).

TABLE II. *Helium Emission Spectrum*

Color	Violet	Blue	Green	Yellow	Red
Wavelength -	4026 (w)	4388 (w)	4922 (w)	5876 (s)	6678 (s)
	4121 (w)	4471 (m)	5016 (m)		7065 (w)
(Strength)	4144 (w)	4713 (w)	5048 (w)		

Procedure

The light sources used in the experiment are in the form of long, narrow glass tubes, known as Geissler tubes, which contain various gases at low pressure. The characteristic emission spectra of these gases can be observed when a high voltage (approximately 5000 volts) electric discharge is passed through them. *Be careful when handling the tubes and do not to touch the terminals.* In addition to helium and hydrogen, we shall examine the spectra from several other gaseous sources to observe the rich variety of spectra emitted by different atoms.

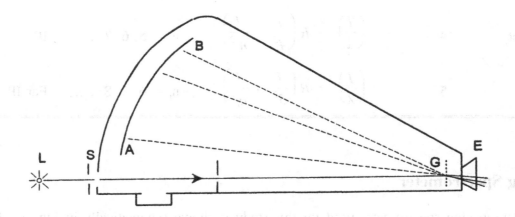

Figure 1: *Grating Spectroscope*

Calibration of the Spectrometer

i)   Mount the helium spectrum tube in front of the entrance slit of the spectroscope and adjust the slit width until the observed spectral lines are sufficiently intense. (Only the first-order spectrum is observed with this spectroscope, the higher-order spectra occuring at angles too large to be observed in the instrument.)

ii)   Although the helium violet lines may not be easily observed, the remaining nine lines which are known to occur in the visible region should be readily identified. Record carefully the position of each of these lines on the scale (to the nearest quarter of a division) and tabulate the scale readings against corresponding wavelength. These results can now be plotted on a linear scale to provide a *calibration curve* for that particular instrument. Be sure to connect the data points with a fine, smooth curve. The accuracy of future wavelength measurements will be dependent on the accuracy of this calibration curve.

Hydrogen Emission Spectrum

iii)   Replace the helium tube with one containing hydrogen. Record the positions on the scale of the three prominent lines corresponding to the H_α, H_β, H_γ Balmer transitions, and determine their wavelengths from the calibration curve.

Other Sources

vii)   Several other low-pressure gaseous sources are available (e.g., argon, krypton, mercury, neon, oxygen, xenon, air) for further study. Use your spectrometer to observe the colors, relative intensities and wavelengths of the lines for each source, recording your observations in your laboratory book. Identify each source by comparing the observed spectra to those on the posted spectral chart or other provided charts.

Analysis

i)   Using the measured wavelength for each of the Balmer transitions, calculate a value for the Rydberg constant. How well does the average value agree with the accepted value?

ii)   Using the accepted value for R, calculate the wavelengths for the H_α, H_β, H_γ hydrogen lines using the series formulae. Compare these with your measured values.

iii)   Using equation 1), calculate the energies of the ground and first eight excited levels in hydrogen (n=1 to 9). From these values, draw (to scale) an energy level diagram for hydrogen and indicate on this all the Balmer transitions. Identify the H_α, H_β, H_γ lines.

Questions

1.   In each series of the hydrogen spectrum (Table I), the wavelength separation between adjacent lines decreases as the wavelength decreases (i.e., as n increases). Each series of lines therefore converges to a so-called *series limit*. Calculate the wavelength for the Balmer series limit. What part of the spectrum does this wavelength occur in.

2.   The Rydberg constant is related through Bohr's theory to other fundamental constants by the formula:

$$R = \frac{2\pi^2 m}{h^3 c}\left(\frac{e^2}{4\pi\,\varepsilon_0}\right)^2$$

where m and e are the mass and charge of the electron, h is Planck's constant, c is the velocity of light and ε_o is the permitivity constant. Calculate R using the known values for these constants.

Name: _____   Partner(s): _____

_____

TABLE I: *Helium spectrum calibration of spectrometer.*

Color										
Scale Reading										
Known Wavelength										

TABLE II: *Measurements of Hydrogen Balmer series.*

Color	Red	Blue	Violet
Scale Reading			
Measured Wavelength			

TABLE III: *Measurements of Spectral Tube A*

Color										
Scale Reading										
Measured Wavelength										

TABLE IV: *Measurements of Spectral Tube B.*

Color										
Scale Reading										
Measured Wavelength										

Signature of Instructor: _____

_____   _____   _____
      Your Name   **Course and Section**   **Date**

_____   _____
      Partner's Name   **Instructor**

21. Kinematics of Linear Motion with Constant Acceleration

Objective: Displacement, velocity and acceleration as functions of time are studied for linear motion with constant acceleration.

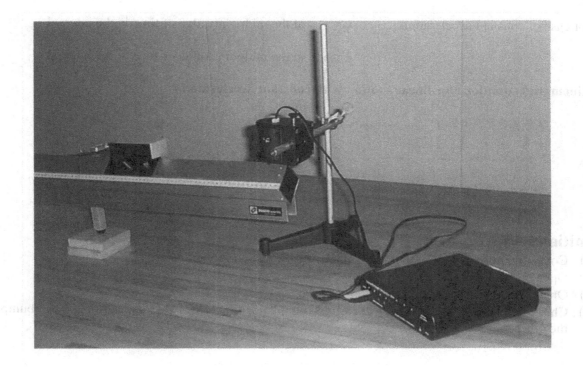

Description: Kinematics is the branch of mechanics that deals with the description of motion of an object. Describing the motion of the object consists of taking into account where it is relative to a reference point, determining the direction it is moving, determining how fast it is going, and determining how fast its velocity is changing i.e. its acceleration.

The apparatus consists of a nearly frictionless "car" which glides on an inclined air track providing a physical situation of constant acceleration in one dimension. A position-measuring sensor monitors the location of the car throughout its motion. The data set is manipulated by the **Data Studio** software by taking successive position differences and dividing by the corresponding time interval in order to obtain the velocity at the midpoint of the time interval. Similarly, differences in successive velocity values divided by the time interval determines the acceleration at the midpoint in time.

Definitions:

instantaneous velocity = $v = dx/dt$ average velocity = $v_{ave} = \Delta x/\Delta t$

instantaneous acceleration = $a = dv/dt$ average acceleration = $a_{ave} = \Delta v/\Delta t$

For case of constant acceleration: $v = v_{ave}$ at the midpoint value of time in the interval

                                    $a = a_{ave}$ at the midpoint value of time in the interval

Kinematics equations for linear motion with constant acceleration:

$$x = x_o + v_o\, t + \tfrac{1}{2}\, a\, t^2 \quad\text{................................ 1)}$$

$$v = v_o + a\, t \quad\text{..2)}$$

$$v^2 = v_o^2 + 2\, a\, (x - x_o) \quad\text{............................3)}$$

Initial Setup:
a) Connect motion sensor to digital channels 1(yellow) and 2(black).
b) Open the "Force" folder.
c) Open the "Force-kinematics.ds" file.
d) Check that the air "car" has a cardboard tab on the position sensor side and a rubber-band bumper on the other side.

Procedure:

Table 1: Calculation of velocity and acceleration.

t_{graph} (s)	x (m)	$\Delta x/\Delta t$ (m/s)	v_{graph} (m/s)	$\Delta v/\Delta t$ (m/s^2)	a_{graph} (m/s^2)	v (m/s)

a) Set up Table 1 (FORMAT 1) with the headings above.

b) Set angle somewhere between 6° and 12°. (Each setup in the lab should be at a different angle.)

c) Set the car about 50 cm from the position sensor and release. Click **Start**. After a few collisions click **Stop**.

d) The position, velocity, and acceleration are displayed as functions of time (Graph 1). Highlight on the velocity graph a straight-line region between successive collisions.

e) Click the 'scale to fit' button on the toolbar above to display mostly the highlighted region. Now highlight the equivalent regions of the position data set (and click on 'scale to fit') and the acceleration data set (and expand vertically).

f) For the highlighted acceleration click on statistics and calculate the mean.

g) For the highlighted velocity click on fit and choose linear fit. The slope is the acceleration. Compare slope value to the mean value for the acceleration.

h) For the highlighted position click on fit and choose quadratic. Double click on the fit box and remove the check from the top box, then accept. The value of A should be half the value of the acceleration. Compare this acceleration value to the two previous values.

i) Print out these three graphs together in landscape and indicate the comparison of the three acceleration values right on the graph.

j) Now remove the three highlighted regions and choose a more limited highlighted region, starting at a small positive velocity and ending near the top of the straight-line region.

k) Proceed as you did above with the acceleration and position graphs and print out these three graphs.

l) Print out separate position, velocity, and acceleration tables for these limited highlighted regions.

Analysis:

Velocity and Acceleration:

a) From printed tables select three successive values of time and position near the beginning of the recorded motion (with small velocity) and copy them into the first three rows of Table 1.

b) These three x values provide two "intervals" in displacement. Calculate $\Delta x/\Delta t$ for each interval and place these calculated average velocities as two entries in Table 1 (rows 1 and 3). These two calculated velocities equal the instantaneous velocities at the midpoint time values.

c) Now calculate $\Delta v/\Delta t$ and place its value in the second row. This will give an average acceleration for that time interval. This value equals the instantaneous acceleration at the midpoint time. This midpoint time is the time written in the second row.

d) Check the printed table to see that the two velocity values agree. Copy these two values into Table 1 under v_{graph} (rows 1 and 3).

e) Check the printed table to see that the acceleration value agrees. Copy this value into Table 1 under a_{graph} (row 2).

f) Now choose three successive values of time and position near the bottom of the plane (larger velocity) and copy the time and position values into Table 1. Skip a row between the first set and this set of values. Repeat b), c), d) and e) for these entries.

g) Average the two velocity values ($\Delta x/\Delta t$) and place in Table 1 under v in the second row of each set. **Note** that the x and v values are **both** at time t_{graph}.

h) The slope of the velocity graph is the acceleration for this data set. Write "slope = a = value"m/s from the linear fit to the velocity graph on one of the lines above Table 1.

Extended Analysis:

Testing the kinematics equations:

a) Calculated values from Table 1 will now be used to write specific kinematics equations for the present motion.
b) In space below Table 1 write the three equations as explicit functions of time using from the first "set"the value of v (last column) as the initial velocity, the slope value written above Table 1 as the acceleration, and the second row position value as x_o.
c) Now predict the final x and v at the bottom of the incline (second "set" values) by giving a value for time. For time, t, use the time interval between the "initial" and "final" values (from second row of each "set") since the equations assume that $t = 0$ when $v = v_o$ and $x = x_o$.
d) How well do these calculations agree with the Table 1 "final" values for x and v?

Quadratic dependence of displacement on time:

a) Write the equation $x = A (t_{graph})^2 + B(t_{graph}) + C$. Calculate an equation in terms of t by substituting $t_{graph} = t + t_o$. The time value t_o is the second row value from the first "set". Initially you will have six terms which will be combined to give a coefficient for t^2, a coefficient for t, and a constant.
b) Compare the coefficients and constant in this equation to those for the previous quadratic equation for x written when "Testing the kinematics equations" above. These coefficients should agree quite well.
c) To exit the experiment, click **File** and then **Quit**, choosing **No** when prompted to save activity.

Questions:

1) Name the function that describes the position versus time graph.
2) Explain the similarities and differences that would occur if you compared your results to a setup using a larger angle of inclination.
3) What is the limit for the value of acceleration that could be obtained from this setup?

Your Name	Course and Section	Date

Partner's Name	Instructor

22. Dynamics of Motion Down an Incline

Objective: The force and acceleration for a cart accelerated down an inclined plane is studied as a function of the angle of incline.

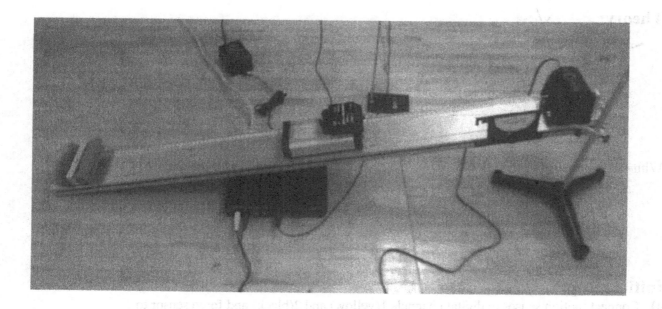

Description: The force that the cart experiences on an incline and the cart's acceleration down the incline will each be measured as a function of angle. The experimental arrangement is depicted in the figure below. The force is first measured by attaching a string to the hook on the force detector and holding the cart with its force detector attached stationary. Then the motion sensor will measure position, velocity and acceleration as a function of time. Although force depends on the mass of the cart system, the acceleration does not.

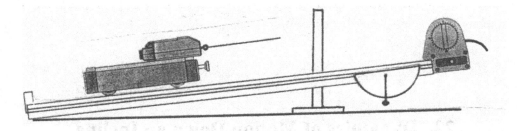

Equipment: Force sensor, motion sensor, track, cart, angle indicator, height adjuster, string, foam bumper, ring stand, balance

Theory:

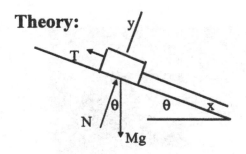

With cart stationary:

$$\Sigma F_x = Ma$$
$$-T + Mg \sin\theta = 0$$
$$T = Mg \sin\theta \ldots\ldots 1)$$

With cart accelerating (T = 0):

$$\Sigma F_x = Ma$$
$$Mg \sin\theta = Ma$$
$$a = g \sin\theta \ldots\ldots\ldots 2)$$

Initial setup:
a) Connect motion sensor to digital channels 1(yellow) and 2(black) and force sensor to analog channel A.
b) Open the "Force" folder.
c) Open the "Force-Newton's second law.ds" file.

Procedure:

Table 1: Measured and calculated acceleration and force

θ (degrees)	sin θ	a_{meas} (m/s^2)	F_{meas} (N)	g sin θ (m/s^2)	M g sin θ (N)	Δa(%)	ΔF(%)

a) Set up Table 1 with the headings above.
b) Measure mass of the cart with force sensor attached and record on one of the lines above Table 1.
c) Press the tare button on the force sensor to zero the unit under condition of no tension.
d) Set angle to 5° and hold cart stationary on the incline with a string running parallel to the incline plane.
e) Use **Data Studio's monitor** feature under the **Experiment** dropdown menu to check the value of the force. Record the value in the force display as the measured force F_{meas} in Table 1.
f) Remove string from force detector and drape wire on the force detector over the ring stand so it does not to interfere with the motion.
g) Bring cart about 60 cm above the foam bumper. Click **Start**, then release the cart. Click **Stop** after the cart hits the bumper.
h) Display the position, velocity, and acceleration as a function of time. Expand the three graphs to nearly fill the available space by **clicking and dragging** along each axis on the displayed units.
i) Highlight the region of constant slope in the velocity graph by **clicking and dragging** in the graph.
j) Click the **Fit** button and choose **linear** fit in the pulldown menu. Record the slope as the measured acceleration a_{meas}. in Table 1.
k) Print out the graphs of x, v and a for the 5° data set.
l) Increase the angle by 3° and repeat steps e) to l). Repeat until one gets to 20°. Print out only a couple of selected cases of the x, v, and a graphs as a function of time (e.g. 11° and 20°).
m) Under the Data palette **click on linear fit** and hit the **delete key** to remove the old fit.
n) Other features of **Data Studio** will be exercised using this data set. **Do not exit** experiment until the end of the lab period.

Analysis:

a) Calculate the theoretical values for the acceleration (eqn. 2) and the force (eqn. 1) and place them in Table 1.
b) Calculate the percent difference for the acceleration and force between the measured and theoretical values and enter in Table 1.
c) Double click on "F vs. a" Table at bottom of the screen and insert the a_{meas} and F_{meas}. values.
d) Double click the Force vs. Acceleration graph at bottom of screen.
e) **Click and drag** in graph to highlight all data points. Click **Fit** button, and choose **linear** fit in the pulldown menu.
f) Print out the fitted F_{meas}. vs. a_{meas}. graph. Write "slope = mass of cart system = value" in one of the lines provided above Table 1.
g) Compare the slope value to the measured mass of the cart system.
h) To exit the experiment, click **File** and then **Quit**, choosing **No** when prompted to save activity.

Questions:

1) Assuming an angle uncertainty of ±0.5°, calculate the uncertainty in acceleration and in force as percentages for the 5° case and for the 20° case. How do these calculated uncertainties compare to the percentage differences calculated in the table?

2) Based on the tabulated values and answers to question 1, is friction a major contributor to the uncertainties? At what angles do you expect the effects of friction to be the greatest?

3) Consider the accelerated motion of an Atwood's machine with the pulley massless and frictionless.
   a) In the figure below, draw free body diagrams for each mass labeling the forces and including appropriate Cartisian coordinate systems for each mass.
   b) Write Newton's second law equations for each mass. Here use symbols only.
   c) Solve for the acceleration of the masses and the tension in the string.
   d) If m_1=2kg and m_2=5kg, calculate the acceleration and the tension.
   e) If the masses have an initial speed of 1.3m/s, how far will they move in 3 seconds and what will be their speed?

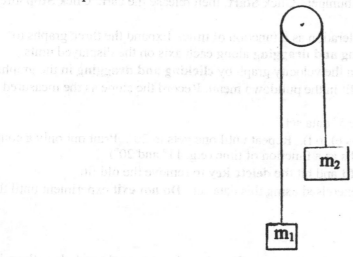

_____   _____   _____
Your Name   Course and Section   Date

_____   _____
Partner's Name   Instructor

23. Impulse and Momentum in Collisions

Objective: Elastic and inelastic collision experiments are performed to gain an understanding of the force integral as the cause of the change in momentum of an object. An impulse approach to collisions suggests ways to increase survivability in a car accident. These strategies are tested in simple air-bag collisions.

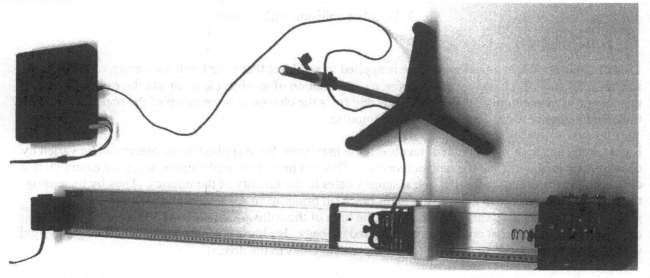

Fig. 1. Collision apparatus used in impulse experiments.

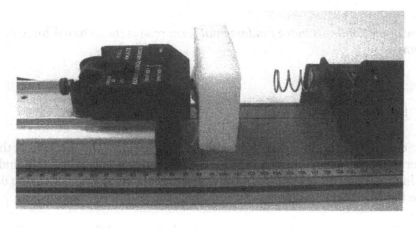

Fig. 2. Detail of collision with a spring.

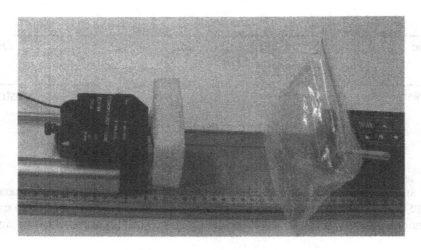

Fig. 3. Detail of collision with air bag.

Description: When an external force is applied to an object that object will accelerate. A more fundamental way of relating an external force to the motion of an object is to equate the external force to the change in momentum of the object. Thus one finds the change in momentum of the object is equal to the time integral of force which is called the impulse.

For a given change in momentum of an object, the maximum force applied to the object can be varied by changing the length of time the collision occurs. This has important implications, since for example, in a car crash, the maximum force that one sustains relates to the severity of the injuries. Thus by increasing the time that this change in momentum takes place (in bringing an accident victim to zero velocity), the greater the survivability. This lengthening of the time of the collision is achieved through seat belts, crumple zones in the front end of the vehicle, and air bags. Building a vehicle extremely strong and rigid would result in the opposite effect, a car far more dangerous to the driver!

Equipment: Force sensor, position sensor, weight, string, rubber bands, air bag, collision car, track, weight scale, pressure sensor

Theory:
Newton's second law of motion in its more fundamental form relates the external force on an object to its change in momentum.

$$\mathbf{F} = d\mathbf{p}/dt$$

Therefore $\int \mathbf{F}\, dt = \int d\mathbf{p} = m\mathbf{v}_f - m\mathbf{v}_i$ 1)

The right side of the equation is the change in momentum of the object. The left side of the equation is the integral of force over time. On a force versus time graph, this integral equals the area under that curve. For a given change in momentum, the maximum force experienced by the object can be decreased by lengthening the time the collision takes place.

For collisions in one dimension, the vector notation can be dropped and the +x or −x direction of the velocities can be introduced by appropriate signs on values:

$$\int F\, dt = \int dp = mv_f - mv_i \quad \text{for 1-D motion}$$ 2)

where the velocities are either positive or negative depending if they are in +x or –x direction.

In a 1-D elastic collision,

$$mv_f = -mv_i$$

hence $$\int F\, dt = -2mv_i \hspace{3cm} 3)$$

In a 1-D totally inelastic collision (where object is brought to rest by the force),

$$\int F\, dt = -mv_i \hspace{3cm} 4)$$

Initial Setup:

a) Study Figures 1) and 2) on the title page to become familiar with the experimental setup.
b) The force sensor wire plugs into analog channel A on the interface box.
c) The motion sensor wire plugs into analog channel B on the interface box.
d) An optional pressure sensor can be added into analog channel C on interface box.
e) Open the "Force" folder.
f) Open the "ImpulseLinear.ds" file.

Procedure and Analysis:

A) Impulse integral in "elastic" collisions with springs.

a) Three collisions will be performed with the light spring and two collisions with the heavier spring.
b) "Weigh" the mass of the cart with the force detector attached by bringing scale over to your setup. Make certain that the scale has been zeroed. Write down this mass value.
c) Screw in the light spring as the "bumper". Check that wire will not adversely affect the velocity just before and after the collision by performing some practice collisions rather gently.
d) Click **START** and press the **Tarr** button on the force detector to make sure it graphs as a zero force initially, then give the car some speed, let it undergo a collision, then click **STOP**.
a) Clear the graph by pulling down **EXPERIMENT** menu and deleting all runs.
e) Highlight the collision region on the velocity graph, click on **auto scale,** then further adjust the horizontal scale so this collision portion occupies about 20-30% of the graph.
f) Now reset your highlighted region to include velocities just before and just after the collision.
g) Under statistics, get the maximum (initial velocity) and the minimum (final velocity) displayed.
h) On the force graph, highlight the peak. Click the **Equations Icon** and select **Area** to perform the impulse integral in Newton-seconds.
i) Print the graph out in landscape.
j) On this graph, label as light spring, then calculate the magnitude of the change in momentum

$$|\Delta p| = m\,|v_f + v_i| \hspace{3cm} 5)$$

k) Alongside this calculated value write the force integral value for comparison.
l) Now repeat for different initial velocities two more collisions with the light spring and two collisions with the heavy spring, labeling and performing the calculations on each printout.

B) Collision employing an air bag.

a) The setup in Figure 3 is now used. The zip-lock air bag is inflated by blowing air into the bag using a straw with the zipper open about 3cm. A small piece of tape stabilizes the air bag.

b) An ideal air-bag collision would bring the cart to rest without giving it a recoil velocity. This will be a trial and error process where the zipper can be opened or closed somewhat to approximate this condition.

c) Click **START** then zero the force sensor with the **Tarr** button. Perform a collision then click **STOP**.

d) Proceed as before, highlighting and expanding the collision region. Check that the final velocity is about zero. Otherwise delete this run (under **EXPERIMENT**) and repeat.

e) Print out graph in landscape and perform calculations and comparisons as before.

f) Repeat this procedure for two other air-bag collisions.

g) Also perform two collisions with the air bag removed.

h) Compare the maximum forces that occur in each case with those experienced in the air-bag collisions. Do you see the benefit of the air bag in the collision?

Questions:

1) Explain the physics of a car crash and how the crumple zone, safety belt, and air bag work in concert to increase the driver's survivability.

2) Compare the average force experienced by a 60kg person moving at 34km/h (20mph) being stopped in a distance of 2cm in one case (e.g. a padded dashboard) or 40cm in the other case (e.g. the effective distance due to the crumple zone and air bag).

3) If a pressure sensor were incorporated in the experiment, a similar profile to the force impulse should be recorded. Since in this experiment, no crumple zone is included, the air bag must dissipate all the energy in the collision. If p is the overpressure during the collision and V is the volume of vented air, the dissipated energy should be given by the integral

$$\int p \, dV$$

which would be the area under the pressure vs volume graph. Choose the air bag collision with the highest initial velocity. Assume all the initial kinetic energy is dissipated by the air bag and the average overpressure is 850Pa (Pa is an SI unit called the pascal). What volume of air (in m^3) was pushed out of the bag? Convert your answer to cubic centimeters.

_____   _____   _____
        Your Name   Course and Section   Date

_____   _____
      Partner's Name   Instructor

24. Properties of a Vertical Spring-Mass System

Objective: The kinematics (position, velocity, acceleration as functions of time) and dynamics (Newton's second law) is studied for the oscillating spring-mass system.

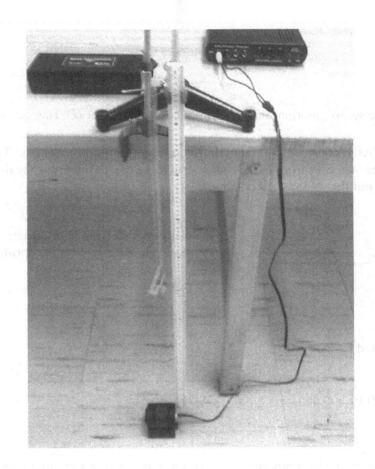

Description: The spring-mass system is hung from the force sensor and "viewed" by the motion sensor placed on the floor as shown in the figure below. The force detector is "zeroed" when the mass is stationary at the equilibrium position. The mass is then displaced downward from the equilibrium position and released. The force, position, velocity and acceleration are then recorded for several oscillations. Then the suspended mass is changed and the experiment is repeated giving rise to a new set of measurements and a new period of oscillation.

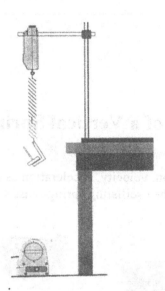

Equipment: Force sensor, motion sensor, spring, mass and hanger set, ring stand

Theory: For simplicity, consider a horizontal, frictionless spring-mass system. The equations derived below will apply to the vertical spring-mass system providing one defines x as the displacement from the equilibrium position (**not** the unstretched position).

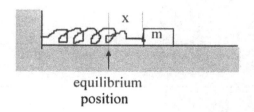

equilibrium
position

x = displacement from equilibrium
$F = -kx$ = Hooke's law for the spring.................. 1)

For the mass accelerated by the spring:

$$\Sigma F_x = ma$$
$$-kx = ma = m\,(d^2x/dt^2)\dots\dots\dots\dots 2)$$

Equation of motion:

$$d^2x/dt^2 + (k/m)x = 0 \quad \text{has solution} \quad x = x_m \cos(\omega t + \varphi),$$

where x_m = amplitude of oscillation
ω = angular frequency
φ = phase constant

The angular frequency ω in the solution must be set to

$$\omega = \sqrt{\frac{k}{m}}$$

But $\omega = 2\pi f = 2\pi/T$ ....3)

where f is the frequency and T is the period of oscillation.

$$\therefore \ T = 2\pi\sqrt{\frac{m}{k}} \quad ....4)$$

The other kinematics equations (v and a) are obtained by differentiating the displacement equation. (Here for simplicity, set $\varphi = 0$, hence $x = x_m$ at t = 0):

$x = x_m \cos(\omega t)$................................5)

$v = dx/dt = - x_m \ \omega \sin(\omega t)$................6)   and thus $v_m = x_m \ \omega$................7)

$a = dv/dt = - x_m \ \omega^2 \cos(\omega t)$ ....8)   and thus $a_m = x_m \ \omega^2$ ....9)

Energy conservation:

$E = K + U = $ constant   where E = mechanical energy of spring-mass system
                                                       K = kinetic energy of the mass
                                                       U = potential energy of the spring

$$E = \tfrac{1}{2}\,mv^2 + \tfrac{1}{2}\,kx^2 = \tfrac{1}{2}\,mv_m^2 = \tfrac{1}{2}\,kx_m^2 ....10)$$

Initial setup:
a) Connect the motion sensor to digital channels 1(yellow) and 2(black) and the force sensor to analog channel A.
b) Open the "Force" folder.
c) Open the "Force-spring-masslab.ds" file.

Procedure:

A: *Measurement of Stretch of Spring for Different Forces*

Table 1: Force vs. Stretched Distance

m (kg)	F = mg (N)	l (m)	L = l_{max} – l (m)

a) Using a **FORMAT 2** sheet, fill in the headings for Table 1.
b) In Table 1 fill in the column for the hanging mass (m) to be used beginning with 25 grams (.025 kg) (mass added = 20 grams, hanger = 5 grams). Increment the hanging mass by 20 grams until reaching 115 grams (.115 kg). Complete the force (F) column.
c) On the desktop click on **Force** icon, then click on **Force-Spring-Mass-Lab** icon. A table F-vs.-L will appear on the screen.
d) At the bottom of the screen <u>expand</u> the window labeled **y, v, a-vs.-t**. Click on button just to the right of the **STATISTICS** icon (Σ) and click on '**mean**' in the pulldown menu.
e) Start by placing a 20 gram mass on the hanger and <u>stabilize</u> it at its new equilibrium position. Use the **START** and **STOP** button to record the mass's position for a brief period (about **10** seconds). Repeat the measurement if there are any spikes in the position graph.
f) Record the position (mean value) as l in the Table 1.
g) Repeat this procedure for the other four masses.
h) Spread out the position versus time plots and print the graph as a record of the l values.
i) Fill in the column L = l_{max} - l in Table 1. The l_{max} value is the top value in the l column.
j) Fill in the F-vs.-L table on the screen using your values from Table 1 (be sure to use **L** and not l).
k) At the bottom of the screen expand the window for the graph of F-vs-L.
l) Click the **Fit** icon and choose **linear**. Write "**slope**" = **k** = '**value**' N/m on a line above Table 1.
m) Print out and label this fitted F-vs.-L graph. Minimize the graph.

B: *Measuring Simple Harmonic Motion*

Table 2. "Measured" Values

m (kg)	T (s)	f = 1/T (Hz)	$\omega = 2\pi f$ (rad/s)	x_m (m)	v_m (m/s)	a_m (m/s^2)	F_m (N)

a) Place 50 grams (total of 55) on the hanger and gently lower the mass to the equilibrium position.
b) At the bottom of the screen expand the window labeled **y, v, a vs. t**.
c) Click **START** and zero the force sensor by pressing and holding for a second its '**TARE**' button. Click **STOP**. Delete the data set. The measured force will then equal the restoring force of the spring (returning the mass to its equilibrium position).
d) Set the spring gently oscillating in the vertical direction. Click **START** to begin recording y-vs.-t, v-vs.-t, a-vs.-t, and F-vs.-t values for at least 20 oscillations and then click **STOP**.
e) Expand each graph by clicking **Scale to Fit** icon for each graph, then print combined graphs in landscape.

f) Use the 'Smart Tool – cross hair' feature to determine the time for about 20 complete oscillations. Divide the time difference by the number of cycles to obtain the period **T**. Show calculation alongside the graph. Record value of **T** in Table 2 and also calculate and record values for **f** and **ω**.

g) Highlight about two cycles of the <u>position vs. time</u> graph.

h) Click on '**scale to fit**' icon on the toolbar and do the highlight the equivalent regions for the other three graphs.

i) Expand each of the graphs vertically to nearly fill the available space. <u>Print</u> out the four graphs using the landscape format. Be sure to label printouts with the value of the mass.

j) Show calculations of amplitudes x_m, v_m, a_m, F_m alongside graphs. (To obtain an amplitude take the difference between the maximum and minimum values and divide by two.)

h) Transfer these values to Table 2.

j) Delete all the data.

k) Repeat steps a) through j) for total masses of 75 grams and 105 grams.

l) Exit experiment by going to **File** and then click on **Quit**, choosing **No** when prompted to save this activity.

Analysis:

Table 3. "Derived" values.

m (kg)	$\omega = (k/m)^{1/2}$ (rad/s)	$T = 2\pi/\omega$ (s)	$v_m = x_m\omega$ (m/s)	$a_m = x_m\omega^2$ (m/s^2)	$F_m = ma_m$ (N)

a) Using a second **FORMAT 2** sheet, fill in the headings as shown above. **Re-label** the table to be Table 3.

b) Using the x_m values from Table 2 calculate and record the derived values for Table 3.

Table 4. Comparison between "measured" and "derived" values.

m (kg)	$\Delta\omega$ % diff.	ΔT % diff.	Δv_m % diff.	Δa_m % diff.	ΔF_m % diff.

c) Use the headings above for the second table (re-label it Table 4) and compare the "measured" and "derived" values for ω, **T**, v_m, a_m, and F_m as percentage differences.

Extended Analysis:

d) Using your "measured" values from Table 2 compare the maximum spring potential energy $E = \frac{1}{2} kx_m^2$ with the maximum kinetic energy of the mass $E = \frac{1}{2}mv_m^2$.

e) Assuming motion begins (t = 0) at maximum displacement (x = x_m), write x, v, and a as explicit functions of time for one of the three measured cases. Specify this case by its mass value. Here insert the measured values for x_m and ω into equations 5, 6, and 8.

f) Choose one data point in the graph at about half the amplitude and get the displacement * and the velocity from the corresponding graphs at that point in time. Then for that point calculate the potential energy of the spring, the kinetic energy of the mass, and the total energy of the system. (See equation 10). Compare the total energy to values in Table 3.

  *Note that the x value is not the position value but rather the displacement from the equilibrium position (the mean value of x).

Your Name	Course and Section	Date
Partner's Name		Instructor

25. Circular Motion and Centripetal Force

Objective: The dependence of the centripetal force on mass, radius, and angular velocity will be studied by rotating masses in horizontal circular paths at constant angular velocities.

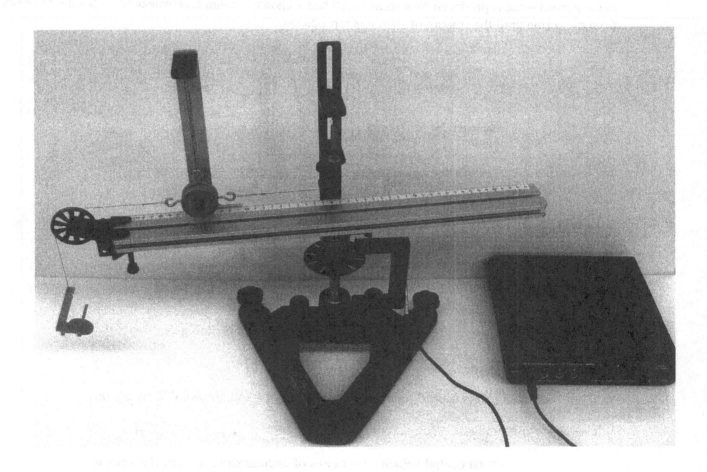

Description: A mass traveling at a constant speed around a horizontal circular path requires a radial inward force called the centripetal (center seeking) force that is constant in magnitude but ever changing in direction (always pointing toward the center of the circular path). Here the only effect of the force is to change the direction of the mass (hence a circular "orbit") but not the speed of the mass. The force vector always remains perpendicular to the velocity vector throughout the circular motion.

The centripetal force depends linearly on the mass and the radius of the orbit and on the square of the angular velocity. This dependence is tested in three ways:

i) The centripetal force is varied keeping the mass and the radius constant.

ii) The mass is varied keeping the centripetal force and the radius constant.

iii) The radius is varied keeping the mass and the centripetal force constant

In each of the above cases, the rotational period is measured and the angular velocity calculated from this period.

A comparison between the measured radial inward force and the calculated centripetal force is made. The radial inward force is produced by a spring stretched a known amount and measured by hanging masses from the spring until the amount of stretch is reproduced.

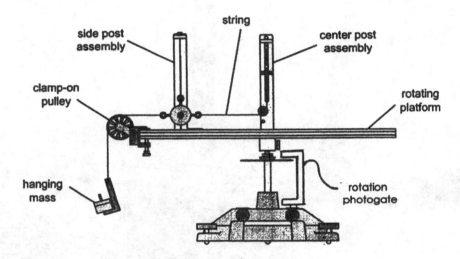

Theory: Newton's second law applied in the radial inward direction gives

$$F_r = m\, a_r \dots\dots\dots\dots\dots\dots\dots\dots\dots\dots\dots\dots\ 1)$$

F_r = centripetal force, m = "bob" mass, a_r = radial inward acceleration

Where $a_r = v^2/r = r\,\omega^2 \dots\dots\dots\dots\dots\dots\dots\dots\dots\ 2)$

v = tangential velocity, r = radius of circular path, ω = angular velocity

hence $F_r = m\, r\, \omega^2 \dots\dots\dots\dots\dots\dots\dots\dots\dots\ 3)$

and $\omega = 2\pi / T$ .... 4)

T = period of the circular motion

The spring force will be measured by hanging masses until it stretches a known amount, hence the measured centripetal force will be:

$F_r = F_{spring} = Mg$ ....5)

F_{spring} = force of the spring, M = hanging mass

A comparison between the measured (equation 5) and the calculated (equation 3) as a percent difference is calculated in each case.

$$\Delta F(\%) = 100 \, [Mg - F_r] / Mg ......6)$$

Initial setup:
a) Connect the rotary motion sensor to digital channels 1(yellow) and 2(black).
b) Open the "Force" folder.
c) Open the "Centripetal Force.ds" file.

Procedure: The data studio software and rotary motion sensor provide a convenient way to measure the period of rotation and to check that the angular velocity was held reasonably constant throughout the measurement.

A: The centripetal force is varied keeping the "bob"mass and the radius constant

Table 1: Variable spring force, constant radius, and constant "bob" mass.

M (kg)	Mg (N)	T (s)	ω (rad/s)	$F_r = mr\omega^2$ (N)	ΔF (%)

a) Set up Table 1 (**FORMAT 2**) with the headings above.
b) Measure the mass of the "bob" m and write its value in units (kg) on a line above the table.
c) Set the radius on the apparatus by positioning the vertical arm at the 15cm mark and write this value in units (m) on a second line above the table.
d) Hang a 15g (10g + hanger) mass off the pulley connected to the bob and move the top of the spring until the "bob" mass hangs vertically (aligned with the indicator line). Record this value as 0.015 (i.e. as kg) in the first column of the table.
e) Move the position indicator to align with orange disk.
f) Remove the hanging mass from the "bob" and carefully rotate on the knurled shaft below the apparatus until the orange disk is aligned with the position indicator.
   Do not interfere with the photogate while turning the shaft.
g) The partner should click **Start** while the motion continues with the orange disk held in alignment.

h) After 10 full turns, the counting system of photogate interrupts (10 counts per revolution) automatically stops and displays both a time in seconds and a graph of counts vs time.

i) Divide the time by 10 to get the period and record its value in the table.

j) Check the graph to see that it remained a reasonably straight line indicating that the angular velocity was relatively constant throughout the measurement.

k) Repeat this procedure for 5 additional hanging masses each time increasing the mass by 10 grams.

l) Print out a graph with the six runs displayed and write "Variable spring force" above the graph.

m) Calculate all the remaining values in the various columns.

B. The mass of "bob" is varied keeping the centripetal force and the radius constant.

Table 2: Variable "bob" mass, constant radius, and constant spring force.

Mg (N)	r (m)	m (kg)	T (s)	ω (rad/s)	$F_r = mr\omega^2$ (N)	ΔF (%)

a) Fill in the above headings in the second table on data sheet and write the descriptive title above this table.

b) Choose the 0.540N value for the hanging weight and 0.15m for the radius throughout this set of five different "bob" masses and record these values in this second table.

c) The "bob" mass can be changed by removing or adding brass disks thus obtaining five "bob" masses, m.

d) Follow the same procedure as above except that the spring position is not changed and set only once with the hanging mass of 0.055g. Calculate the values is the various columns for the five different bob masses.

C.) The radius is varied keeping the "bob" mass and the centripetal force constant

Table 3: Variable radius, constant "bob" mass, and constant spring force.

Mg (N)	m (kg)	r (m)	T (s)	ω (rad/s)	$F_r = mr\omega^2$ (N)	ΔF (%)

a) Fill in the above headings in a third table and write the descriptive title above this table.

b) Choose the 0.540N value for the hanging weight and the mass of the "bob" with two brass disks attached (as in Table 1). Record these values in Table 3.

c) The radius will be changed in steps of 1cm from 0.14m to 0.17m, namely four different values, by moving the vertical arm. For each radius, the 0.055kg mass is hung from the "bob", the top of the spring is moved so the "bob" hangs vertically, and the position indicator is aligned with the orange disk.

d) Record data for the four different radii and calculate the remaining values in the table.

Questions:

Calculate the centripetal force for the three examples below. **Before you do the calculations,** guess which case produces the largest centripetal force and which produces the smallest (there are no "wrong" answers here!). Write these guessed answers ahead of your detailed calculations.

1) A ten kilogram rock is in geosynchronous orbit about the earth at the orbital radius of 42 thousand kilometers.

2) A 50g pebble is stuck in the treads of a truck tire of radius 30cm. The truck is traveling at 60 kilometers per hour (about 36 miles per hour).

3) An electron orbits the nucleus at a distance of 5.3×10^{-11}m and makes 6.6×10^{15} revolutions per second.

Your Name	Course and Section	Date

Partner's Name		Instructor

26. Projectile Motion

Objective: The kinematics of projectile motion in the earth's gravitational field will be studied to gain an understanding of horizontal range, maximum height, time of flight, and trajectory of the projectile.

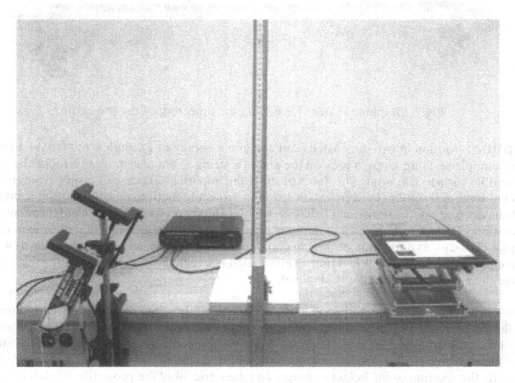

Fig.1. Apparatus for measuring initial speed, time-of-flight, horizontal range, and maximum height of the projectile as a function of launch angle.

Caution! Safety glasses must be worn during this experiment.

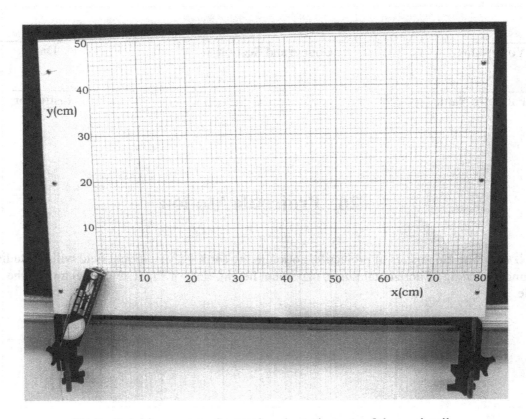

Fig.2. Graphing system for tracing the trajectory of the projectile.

Description: Motion in two dimensions can come in a variety of examples: motion on a simple roller coaster, a stunt plane doing loops, a rock on the end of a string in circular motion, a rocket being sent from the earth's surface into orbit. This lab will study the important 2D case of projectile motion. The gravitational force acts only in the vertical direction in projectile motion, thus the motion is broken into its vertical behavior and into its horizontal behavior which exhibits no force and acts independently of the vertical motion. These two independent motions give rise to position as a function of time in component form (x,y), to velocity as a function of time in component form (v_x, v_y), and to acceleration as a function of time in component form (a_x, a_y). When time is eliminated between the x and y equations, the trajectory or equation of the path of the projectile is obtained.

The motion is determined by the initial velocity and launch angle of the projectile. Measurements will be made of the range of the projectile, the maximum height of the projectile above the launch point, the time of flight of the projectile, and the path (trajectory) that the projectile describes. These will be studied as a function of launch angle. Since the lab requires initiating and ending the run on the computer, the firing of the projectile, the spotting of the height or range, and the retrieval of the projectile, the lab is found to work well with groups of three students per setup.

Equipment: projectile, launcher, 2 photogates, time-of-flight sensor pad, lab jack, horizontal scale, vertical scale, projectile grapher, motion sensor, tracing paper

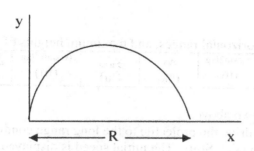

Theory:

x motion: (steps involving integrals are not shown)   y motion:

$$dv_x/dt = a_x = 0$$ $$dv_y/dt = a_y = -g$$

$$dx/dt = v_x = constant = v_o cos\theta$$ $$dy/dt = v_y = v_o sin\theta - gt$$

$$x = (v_o \, cos\theta)t \, ... \, 1)$$ $$y = (v_o sin\theta)t - gt^2/2 \, ... \, 2)$$

Combining 1) and 2), one obtains the equation of the trajectory:

$$y = x \, tan\theta - (gx^2)/2(v_o cos\theta)^2 .... \, 3)$$

The flight time corresponding to the horizontal range is found by setting $y = 0$ in eqn.2.

$$t = 2 \, v_o sin\theta/g \, ... \, 4)$$

The horizontal range is found by substituting eqn.4 into eqn.1.

$$R = v_o^2 sin2\theta/g .... 5)$$

The maximum height of the projectile is found by substituting half the eqn.4 value for t into eqn.2.

$$y_{max} = (v_o sin\theta)^2/2g .... 6)$$

Initial setup:

a) Connect launcher photogate 1 to digital channel 1, launcher photogate 2 to digital channel 2, and time-of-flight sensor pad to digital channel 3.

b) Open the "Force" folder.

c) Open the "Projectile1.ds" file. Two windows are displayed. One will show the projectile's initial speed calculated from the distance and time interval between the two photogates mounted on the launcher. The other window displays the projectile's time-of-flight by registering the time interval between the first gate and the sensor pad.

Procedure and Analysis:

Table 1. Measured and theoretical flight times, horizontal ranges, and maximum heights of the projectile.

θ (deg.)	t (s)	$2v_o\sin\theta/g$ (s)	Δt (%)	R (m)	$v_o^2\sin2\theta/g$ (m)	Δx (%)	y_{max} (m)	$(v_o\sin\theta)^2/2g$ (m)	Δy_{max} (%)

a) Setup Table 1 (FORMAT 1) headings as shown above.
b) Set the angle to zero degrees, use plunger to drive the projectile to the long range condition (three "clicks"), click **Start**, fire the projectile, then click **Stop**. The initial speed is displayed in the appropriate window. No value will display in the time-of-flight window. Repeat this measurement a few times and record the speeds on a line above the table, checking for consistency. Label this the long-range v_o.
c) Repeat this procedure for the intermediate range (two "clicks") case and record the speeds on another line above Table 1. Label this the medium-range v_o.

d) For long-range condition one will measure the flight time t, the horizontal range R, and the maximum height y_{max} for initial angles 10, 20, 30, 45, 60, 70, and 80 degrees. Carbon paper will provide a mark where the projectile strikes. The scale along the edge of the lab bench will provide an efficient way of measuring the range.
e) Adjust the height of the vertical 2m stick so that the attached scale has its zero at the height of the launch point. The measured maximum heights can then be directly read from this scale.
f) Fire the projectile successively, repeating the measurement several times at each angle to check for consistency and obtain an average value for the flight time, the range, and the maximum height. The boxes in the table will accommodate several measured values. Note that launch speeds are not recorded here since the launch angle is no longer zero.
g) Estimate the uncertainty in the range values and the height values and record these estimates above Table 1.
h) Calculate the corresponding theoretical values in the columns alongside the measured values and then calculate the % differences between the calculated and the measured values.

Table 2. Demonstrating the parabolic nature of the trajectory.

θ (deg.)	v_o (m/s)	x (m)	y (m)	y(eqn.3) (m)

i) Setup Table 2 (FORMAT 1) headings as shown above.
j) Set the launcher angle to 70 degrees.
k) Position the plexiglass "graph" with its origin at the launch point and its axes horizontal and vertical.
l) The projectile is fired repeatedly in the short-range (one "click") condition and grid-crossing points are marked with an erasable marking pen. First mark crossings at the 10cm grid lines on the x axis. Then find the intermediate (5cm) grid crossings. Then return and redo the 10cm grid crossings which now will be more accurate.
m) In Table 2 record the x and y coordinates of the marked grid crossings for the trajectory.
n) Using eqn.3, calculate the y values for the parabolic trajectory at these same x values.
o) Plot graph of this parabolic trajectory and fit a smooth curve through these plotted points.
p) Superimpose the measured points (x,y) using a different plotting symbol.

If time permits:

q) Return to your original setup. From Table 1 choose the range at launcher angle of 70 degrees.
r) Using eqn.5 and the initial velocity for the intermediate range (two "clicks"), calculate the new launch angles that would give this same range.
s) Setup to these launch angles and measure the ranges to see how closely they correspond to the chosen range value.
t) Show the details of this calculation and the comparison between the measured and calculated range values in the space below Table 1. Give the calculation a heading, "Duplicating the range with new launch velocity"

If time permits:

u) For a final set of measurements, the launch angle will be set at 60 degrees and the projectile speed will be the long-range condition. Now the floor will be the "target" of the projectile.
v) Perform a test firing and note where the projectile strikes the floor (mark an X with a pencil). Now tape a piece of paper to the floor centered on this mark. Place tracing paper over this sheet and fire the projectile several times. Locate the average of these marks and measure the range using the scale along the table edge by hanging a meter stick vertically. Record this range value as the value of x.
w) Measure the distance from the launch point to the floor, which is the (negative) y value.
x) Now in the equation of the trajectory, substitute in the v_o, θ, and y value and solve for x. Compare to your measured value. You may record your values and show your work in space below Table 2. Give this section a heading "Target placed on floor".

Analysis:

1) In addition to the analysis in above sections, return to the Table 1 and graph the calculated range, maximum height, and time-of-flight vs angle. Add to Table 1 the calculated values at 0° and 90° for graphing purposes. Place all these plots on the same graph using a single vertical scale on the left side for the R and y_{max} and the time scale on the right side of the graph. Connect related points with smooth curves using a set of French curves.

Questions:

1) For an initial velocity of 15m/s and a launch angle of 55 degrees, where will the projectile strike the side of the hill (which makes a slope angle of 20 degrees)?

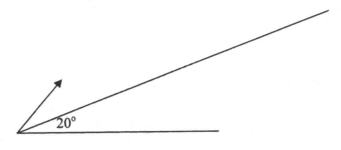

_____   _____   _____
Your Name   Course and Section   Date

_____   _____
Partner's Name   Instructor

27. Microwave Interference and Polarization

Objective: The wavelength of light is determined from the two-slit interference pattern and from the standing wave condition. Polarization is studied as a function of angle.

Fig.1. Apparatus for two-slit interference.

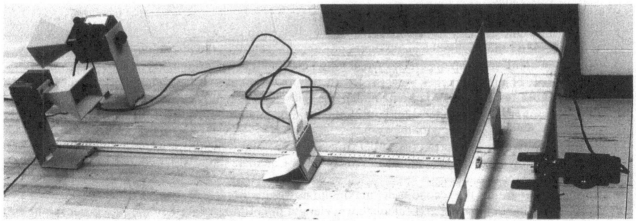

Fig.2. Apparatus for standing wave experiment.

Fig.3. Apparatus for polarization measurement.

Description:

This experiment is a computer interfaced (Data Studio) version of Experiment 11 in the manual. Please read the description with theory presented in that experiment. Since the data recording proceeds so efficiently, the student will now be able to complete:

i) Two slit interference pattern (microwave intensity vs angle measurements for three slit spacings)
ii) Standing wave pattern (microwave intensity vs linear position)
iii) Polarization (microwave intensity vs rotation angle of the microwave detector)

Initial setup:

a) Study the experimental setup in Fig.1.
b) Check that the angle sensor is connected to the digital channels 1and 2.
c) Open the "Waves and Light" folder.
d) Open the "Microwaves1.ds" file.

Procedure:

A. Two slit interference pattern

Table 1: Calculation of wavelength.

max or min	m-value	d (cm)	θ (deg.)	$\lambda = \dfrac{d \sin \theta}{m}$ (cm)	$\lambda = \dfrac{d \sin \theta}{m - \frac{1}{2}}$ (cm)

a) Set up Table 1 (FORMAT 1) with the headings above.
b) Turn on the microwave transmitter (plug it in) and the microwave detector (switch it on).
c) Choose a slit spacer of 6cm and set up slit widths to 2 cm each giving a d = 8cm.
d) Position the detector at zero degrees and adjust the step and variable controls on the detector so the maximum intensity is somewhat less than full scale on the meter when the detector is moved over the +20° to −20° range
e) Position the detector at +60 degrees. Click **Start**.
f) Slowly move the detector from +60° to −60° then click **Stop**.
g) With the **smart tool** locate the angle that represents the center of the distribution.
h) Click on **Calculate** at top of screen. An input window will be superimposed on the graph.
i) Input the offset angle and click **Accept**. The distribution should now be centered. Print out in landscape the 2-slit intensity pattern and label graph with d = 8cm.
j) With the **smart tool** locate the angles of all the maxima and minima and label each maximum and minimum on your printout with these angles.
k) Average the two angles for the first order (m=1) maxima and write this value and 1 for m in your table indicating in column 1 that this is a maximum. Calculate the wavelength based on the equation **in column 5** (for maxima).
l) Repeat procedure for the second order maximum now with m = 2.
m) Now skip a line in the table and calculate wavelength **in column 6** based on the first order minima with m = 1.
n) Repeat the procedure for the second order minima with m = 2.
o) Skip a line in the table.
p) Now setup the two slit system with a slit spacer of 9cm and slit width of 2cm giving a d = 11cm and repeat the entire procedure with calculations as above. If additional peaks are found, carry out the analysis to still higher orders (e.g. m = 3).
q) Skip a line in the table, set up the system as before but with a 15.2cm spacer and slit width of 2cm giving a d = 17.2cm and repeat the above procedure.

B: Standing wave pattern

a) This procedure will be performed on a single separate setup with its own computer. When this apparatus is available, take your transmitter over to the setup (see Fig.2) and place it facing the metal reflector wall with about one meter distance between your transmitter and the metal wall.
b) Open the "Waves and Light" folder.
c) Open the "Microwaves2.ds"file.
d) Click **Start** and slowly move the planar detector along the meter stick guide for a distance of about 30cm. Then click **Stop**.
e) Successive peaks are $\lambda/2$ apart. Locate the positions of two distant peaks in the standing wave pattern, count the number of intervals between these peaks, divide the distance by this number and equate it to $\lambda/2$. Compare your value of λ to that calculated from 2-slit interference.

C: Polarization measurement

a) This procedure will be performed on another single separate setup with its own computer. When this setup is available, take your transmitter over to this apparatus (see Fig.3) and place your transmitter at end of meter stick facing the detector.
b) Open the "Waves and Light" folder.
c) Open the "Microwaves3.ds" file. This will display a graph of the predicted $(\cos \theta)^2$ behavior. You will measure the intensity as a function of angle and compare the measured and predicted angle dependencies.
d) With the detector and transmitter turned on, set the detector at $0°$ and adjust the meter reading so it is nearly full scale.
e) Click **Start** and slowly rotate the detector (in clockwise sense when viewed from its back side) through one full rotation, then click **Stop**.
f) Adjust the vertical scale on the measured intensity to superimpose on the predicted $(\cos \theta)^2$ behavior.
g) Expand the angle scale so the graph of the overlapped region basically fills the screen. Print this graph in landscape and label it Polarization Measurement.

Questions:
Return to the Experiment 11 and answer the questions posed there.

Your Name	Course and Section	Date
Partner's Name		Instructor

28. Diffraction and Interference of Light

Objective: To gain a deeper understanding of the wave nature of light, the diffraction of coherent light from a single slit and the interference of coherent light from a double slit are measured and studied.

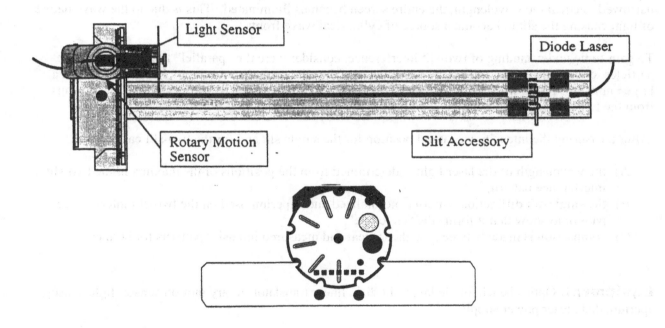

Description: The wave nature of light is demonstrated here by the diffraction of light emanating from a single slit and by the interference of light emanating from two slits. To study these effects, coherent light must impinge on the slits. Coherence simply means that the light should be of a single wavelength and that a fixed phase relation should apply to the system. In case of the two slits, the phase difference remains constant between waves striking one slit and the other. In our experiment, the phase difference of the light striking the two slits is zero.

In Thomas Young's original experiments (in 1810), he first found that sunlight illuminating two closely spaced slits did not produce an interference pattern. This was because each slit was randomly illuminated by light from a different point on the sun. The light illuminating the two slits was in no way "correlated". This is therefore an example of incoherent light. Most conventional light sources are incoherent. Young cleverly got around this problem by first passing the sunlight through a pinhole, establishing a degree of coherence, before sending the light to the double slits. And although the wavelength was not single-valued, a rough interference pattern was observed which established that light could be viewed as a wave.

Currently we are fortunate to have intense sources of coherent light, namely lasers. The diode laser operating in this lab produces a well-collimated beam of coherent light of a single wavelength.

To gain an understanding of diffraction from a single slit, imagine first having the slit opening perhaps 100 x wavelength of the light. "Parallel" light passing through the slit would produce an "image" of the slit on a distant screen that is basically the geometric width of the slit. But as the slit is narrowed down to say 10λ, one finds the image on the screen much broader than the geometric width. And with the slit narrowed to equal the wavelength, the entire screen becomes illuminated. This is due to the wave nature of light causing the slit to become a source of cylindrical wave fronts.

To gain some understanding of two-slit interference, consider were the "parallel" light to behave like particles, one would expect to find the two images of the slits on a distant screen. Instead, one finds a large number of bright lines on the screen. This again can be explained by the cylindrical wave fronts from the two slits interfering with one another at the distant screen.

After measuring the intensity vs. lateral position for the single slit and for the two-slit cases:

   A) the wavelength of the laser light is determined from the positions of the maxima in the two-slit interference pattern,
   B) the single-slit diffraction pattern is normalized and superimposed on the two-slit interference pattern to show that it forms the "envelope",
   C) comparison is made between the theoretical and measured intensity patterns for both cases.

Equipment: Optics bench, diode laser, slit disk, linear translator, rotary motion sensor, light sensor, aperture disk, laser power supply

Theory:

A. Intensity as function of lab angle for the two slit interference pattern without diffraction effects:

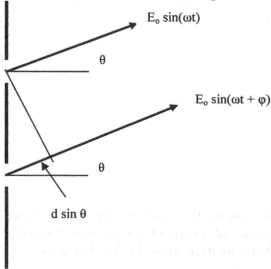

$E_o \sin(\omega t)$

θ

$E_o \sin(\omega t + \varphi)$

θ

d sin θ

At a distant "screen", the two waves are out of phase by phase angle φ due to path length difference of d sin θ. Applying the principle of superposition at the distant "screen"

$E_r(\theta) = E_1 + E_2$
$\quad\quad = E_o \sin(\omega t) + E_o \sin(\omega t + \varphi)$
$\quad\quad = 2 E_o \cos(\varphi/2) \sin(\omega t + \varphi/2)$

$I(\theta) \; \alpha \; [E_r(\theta)]^2$
$\quad\quad \alpha \; 4 E_o^2 \cos^2(\varphi/2) \sin^2(\omega t + \varphi/2)$

Now expressing the intensity in a time averaged manner

$I(\theta) = I_o \cos^2(\varphi/2)$ ....1)

To express the phase angle, φ, in terms of lab angle, θ, recall that

$\dfrac{\text{phase difference}}{2\pi} = \dfrac{\text{path difference}}{\lambda}$

$\dfrac{\Phi}{2\pi} = \dfrac{d \sin \theta}{\lambda}$ ....2)

Intensity maxima will be located where $\cos^2(\varphi/2)$ equals 1, namely:

$\dfrac{\Phi}{2} = \dfrac{\pi d \sin \theta}{\lambda} = n \pi$ where n = 0, 1, 2,...   ....3)

Intensity minima will be located where $\cos^2(\varphi/2)$ equals 0, namely:

$\dfrac{\Phi}{2} = \dfrac{\pi d \sin \theta}{\lambda} = (n + \tfrac{1}{2}) \pi$ where n = 0, 1, 2, ...4)

B. Intensity as function of lab angle for the diffraction from a single slit:

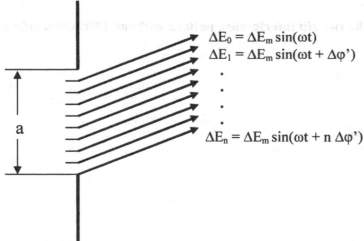

$$\Delta E_0 = \Delta E_m \sin(\omega t)$$
$$\Delta E_1 = \Delta E_m \sin(\omega t + \Delta \varphi')$$
$$\vdots$$
$$\Delta E_n = \Delta E_m \sin(\omega t + n \, \Delta \varphi')$$

The vertical slit viewed from above is bathed in coherent light from the left hand side. The slit is divided up in equal segments, each segment acting as a source of a cylindrical wavefront. On a distant "screen", each electric field element from these segments is phase shifted from its neighbor by $\Delta \varphi'$ due to its slightly longer pathlength (when going from top to bottom).

To apply the principle of superposition to these electric field elements, a phasor diagram is utilized. (At the instant shown, $\omega t = 0$.):

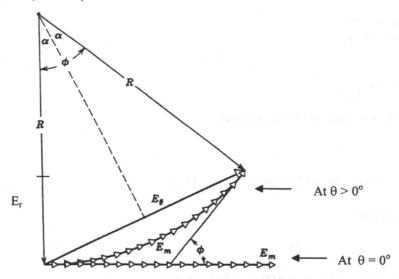

The resultant electric field is the projection of the amplitude E_θ onto the vertical axis.

$$E_r = E_\theta \sin(\omega t + \varphi'/2)$$

To obtain an expression for E_θ, one obtains from the figure above that

$$E_\theta = 2 R \sin(\varphi'/2)$$

$$R = \frac{\text{arc "length"}}{\text{angle}} = \frac{E_m}{\varphi'}$$

Thus $E_\theta = E_m \dfrac{\sin(\varphi'/2)}{\varphi'/2}$

where $\quad E_m = n\Delta E_m$ and $\varphi' = n\Delta\varphi' \quad$ for n very large

The intensity, time averaged, depends on the square of the amplitude

$I(\theta) \alpha [E_\theta]^2$

$I(\theta) = I_o \dfrac{[\sin(\varphi'/2)]^2}{[\varphi'/2]^2}$ ....5)

To get this diffraction intensity as a function of lab angle, recall that

$\dfrac{\text{phase difference}}{2\pi} = \dfrac{\text{path difference}}{\lambda}$

$\dfrac{\Phi'}{2\pi} = \dfrac{a\sin(\theta)}{\lambda}$ ....6)

Diffraction maxima will be located at $\varphi/2 = 0°$ and at

$\dfrac{\Phi'}{2} = \dfrac{\pi a \sin(\theta)}{\lambda} = (n - \frac{1}{2})\pi \qquad$ where n = 1, 2, 3, ...7)

Diffraction minima will be located at

$\dfrac{\Phi'}{2} = \dfrac{\pi a \sin(\theta)}{\lambda} = n\pi \qquad$ where n = 1, 2, 3, ...8)

C. Intensity as function of lab angle for the two-slit interference pattern with diffraction effects

The expression for the diffraction intensity as a function of angle is used to replace the I_o in the two slit interference intensity without diffraction effects giving the corrected intensity:

$I(\theta) = I_o \dfrac{[\sin(\varphi'/2)]^2}{[\varphi'/2]^2} \times \cos^2(\varphi/2)$ ....9)

The frontal factor acts as an "envelope" restricting the height of the local maximum in intensity.

Initial Setup:

a) Study the figure on the title page to become familiar with the experimental setup.
b) The wires from the rotary motion sensor are plugged into digital channels 1 and 2 on the interface box.
c) The light sensor wire plugs into analog channel A on the interface box and the gain on sensor is set to 100.
d) Leave the diode laser power supply turned off initially.
e) Open the "Light" folder. Open the "DiffractionInterference.ds" file.
f) Click on **Setup** → Calibrate Sensor
g) In a darkened room under Calibrate Point 1, click on Read from Sensor → O.K. → close setup (click X). This effectively zero's the sensor.
h) Turn on the diode laser power supply.

Procedure and Analysis:

A) The wavelength of the laser light will be determined from the positions of the maxima in the two-slit interference pattern.

a) Under Displays in the left hand column, double click on "Preview Graph".
b) On the graph, double click on the dialog box in the upper right hand corner and type in the lab partners last names (or if you have your own printer, click on box and delete it. Then simply hand write your names on the graphs as they get printed.).
c) Before taking a data set, practice moving the light sensor in a slow, smooth, and continuous fashion by rotating the pulley on the rotary motion sensor.
d) Choose the double slits with d = 0.25mm (.00025m) and a = 0.04mm (.00004m). Position the slits at the "9 o'clock" position so the laser light passes through and forms an interference pattern of many "lines" on the aperture disk of the light sensor.
e) Rotate aperture slit #2 in front of the light sensor at the "6 o'clock" position.
f) Position the aperture at 6cm and the double slits at 106cm giving a D = 1.0m.
g) Move the light sensor to either end of track.
h) In a darkened room, click **START** and very slowly move the sensor across the interference pattern, then click **STOP**.
i) Inspect the pattern. It should appear smooth and symmetric and have secondary maxima groups on either side of the central grouping with the scale increasing to the right in the usual manner. If this is not the case, pull down **EXPERIMENT** menu and **DELETE** the Last Data Run. Then repeat the measurement procedure.
j) Adjust the distribution so the central grouping fills the graph and print out in landscape.
k) Using the **Smart Tool**, locate the positions of two maxima near opposite sides of the central grouping, y_1 and y_2 and label values in units of meters on the graph.
l) Count the number of "intervals", n, between these chosen maxima and write on graph. Write also the values of d, a and D on graph in units of meters.
m) Locate the maximum position at the very center of this grouping, y_{center} and label on the graph.
n) Calculate the wavelength using

$$\lambda = \frac{d\,(y_2 - y_1)}{n\,D} \quad \ldots\ldots\ldots\ldots\ldots 10)$$

Express this wavelength in units of meters and in units of nanometers, nm.
o) This graph in called Run # 1 in Data Studio.

B) The measured single-slit diffraction pattern will be superimposed on the measured two-slit interference pattern to show that it forms the "envelope".

a) Position the single slit, a = 0.04mm (.00004m), so the laser beam passes through it and forms a diffraction pattern on the aperture disk of the light sensor. Choose aperture slit # 5.

b) The aperture is positioned at 6cm and the single slit is at 106cm giving D = 1.0m.

c) Turn off diode laser.

d) Click on **Setup** → Calibrate Sensor. In a darkened room under Calibrate Point 1, click on Read from Sensor → O.K. → close setup (click X). This effectively zero's the sensor. Turn on diode laser.

e) Scan across this diffraction pattern in the same slow manner, starting from either end of the track, clicking **START** then finally **STOP**.

f) Inspect the pattern to see that it is smooth and symmetric with secondary maxima on either side of the central maximum. If this is not the case, pull down **EXPERIMENT** menu and **DELETE** the Last Run. Then repeat the measurement procedure.

g) Using the **Smart Tool** locate the position, y_{center}, of the distribution.

h) Print graph of the diffraction pattern and on the graph write y_{center}, a, and D in units of meters.

i) This is Run # 2 in Data Studio.

j) The lateral scale will now be converted to lab angles in degrees using the equation

$$\theta = (57.3) \, (y - y_{center})/D \quad \ldots\ldots\ldots\ldots 11)$$

which invokes the small angle approximation and is valid between $-10°$ and $+10°$.

k) Under Displays in the left hand column, double click on "Measured Single Slit with Measured Double Slit".

l) On the graph, double click on the dialog box in the upper right hand corner and type in the lab partners last names (or delete box).

m) Click **Calculate** button at top of screen.

n) Definition should read "Measured Double Slit Angle = …"

o) Click on Please define variable "x" → data measurement → position, ch 1 & 2 (m):Run # 1 → O.K. → Yes

p) Write Distance = 1.0m, Offset = y_{center} value for the double slit case, then click Accept.

q) Now repeat the procedure for single slit in the steps below.

r) Click **Calculate** button at top of screen.

s) Definition should read "Measured Single Slit Angle = …"

t) Click on Please define variable "x" → data measurement → position, ch 1 & 2 (m):Run # 2 → O.K. → Yes

u) Write Distance = 1.0m, Offset = y_{center} value for the single slit case, then click Accept.

v) Adjust the vertical scales so the single slit pattern forms an envelope for the double slit pattern, displays the second order groupings and fills the screen. Print out these superimposed graphs in landscape and write on graph the values for a, d, and λ.

C) Comparison will be made between the theoretical and measured intensity patterns for diffraction and two-slit interference cases.

a) Under Displays in left hand column, double click "Measured Single Slit with Predicted Single Slit"

b) The diffraction equation has been programmed. Values for a and λ must be supplied.

c) Click **Calculate** button at top of screen.

d) Definition should read "Predicted Single Slit = …"

e) Insert values a = .00004m, lambda = calculated wavelength in nanometers, click Accept.
f) Close calculate window (click X).
g) Adjust the two distributions to normalize them and print out.
h) Under Displays in left column, double click on "Measured Double Slit with Predicted Double Slit"
i) Click **Calculate** button at top of screen.
j) Definition should read "Predicted Double Slit = ..."
k) Insert values a = .00004m, lambda = calculated wavelength in nanometers, d = .00025m, click Accept.
l) On the graph, double click on the dialog box in the upper right hand corner and type in the lab partners last names (or delete box).
m) Adjust the scales so that the distributions fill the screen, secondary maxima are displayed, and the experimental and theoretical distributions are normalized to one another. Print out in landscaped and label with a, d, D, and λ.

D) A measured two-slit interference pattern will be measured with known wavelength and slit width (a = .04mm) but unknown slit spacing. Analysis of the pattern will determine the d-value.

a) Repeat the procedure under Section A) using the variable two slit spacing with a = .04mm slit width and a rather wide slit spacing.
b) Using the Equation 10 with the known λ, solve for d.

Questions:

1) Sunlight extends over the full visible range from 400nm to 700nm. Although this light is not monochromatic (single wavelength), Thomas Young in 1870 was still able to view an interference pattern. Carefully describe what you would expect the pattern to look like and how it would differ from the two-slit interference pattern measured with the diode laser.

2) If one were to normalize theoretical graphs at the $0°$ maximum for the two-slit interference cases, how would the pattern differ from your results were a = λ? If you have access to the computers, you can run this case and compare with your calculated intensity in the $-10°$ to $+10°$ range.

3) Although these interference patterns are of great interest, how useful would a two-slit system be in attempting to resolve several different wavelengths emitted by a particular light source. Give considerable detail in your answer.

| Your Name | Course and Section | Date |

| Partner's Name | Instructor |

29. The Stefan-Boltzmann Law of Radiation

Refer to Experiment #14 for the Introduction to this experiment.

Procedure:

Part A. High-Temperature Measurements

At high temperatures the relationship of Eq. (2) should hold. The objective of this laboratory exercise is to demonstrate simply that the power radiated depends on temperature to the fourth power. This can be accomplished without knowing the Stefan-Boltzmann constant σ, the geometrical factor e, or the calibration of the radiation detector. Let T be the temperature and P the radiation intensity; then the relationship between the logarithm of the uncalibrated output of the detector (actually in millivolts) and. the logarithm of the temperature should take the form

$$\ell og P = n \ell og T + K \quad .... 4)$$

Here n is the power of T, and K is a constant that combines all the unknown multipliers.   The essence of Part A of this laboratory exercise is to measure pairs of data consisting of the lamp temperature and the output of the thermopile detector and plot the logarithm of the detector output vs. the logarithm of the temperature. Verification of the Stefan-Boltzmann relationship requires that n, the slope of the plot, should be four.

The apparatus consists of an electric lamp as heat source, thermopile detector to measure the radiation intensity and Data Studio program sblaw1.ds to process the data. The plotting and measuring of the slope can be done manually or with Excel. These components are configured as shown in Figure 1, page 14-4.

Note that the lamp and detector are connected to the computer interface, which enables the computer to display two meters, one showing the temperature in Kelvins, the other showing the detector output in millivolts.

A) Preliminary Steps

a) Do not switch on the power supply at this time. Do rotate the *Volts* knob completely counter clockwise.

b) Carefully inspect the relative placement of the detector and the lamp. They should be aligned and separated by 6 cm. Once their relative position is set DO NOT move them. Should they move all measurements must be discarded\and a new set taken.

c) Open the Data Studio program sblaw1.dslocated in folder Heat. Select *Start* and observe the meters. The temperature meter should read close to room temperature (in Kelvins). The detector meter generally fluctuates. To verify that it is functioning place your warm hand in front of its window (a small circular opening) and note some increase in the detector meter. Select *Stop*.

d) Open Excel and size a new spreadsheet to fit on the computer screen below the Data Studio meters. Place the following column headings in the first row on the spreadsheet beginning at the top left (Column A, Row 1)

Target Temp. (K)	*T* Temp (K)	*P* Intensity (mv)	Log T	Log P

e) Under *Target Temperature* insert 1000 in the next row, then 1177 in the next row, etc adding 177 in each row until 2770 is reached. Then save the Excel spreadsheet on the desktop as St-Bltz.XXYY.xls where XXYY are the initials of the lab partners.

B) Data Gathering

a) Switch on the power supply **immediately switching it off if the lamp lights up**. The lamp should not light if the *Volts* control knob is fully counter clockwise. Select *Start* on Data Studio and observe its *Temperature* meter, which as before should be indicating room temperature. Very gently rotate the *Volts* control knob on the power supply until the computer *Temperature* meter indicates the first target temperature, 1000 K. Generally, because it is difficult to exactly set the target temperature, a temperature close to the target is acceptable. Type the actual temperature value next to the target temperature in the second column headed "*T* Temperature (K)." Watch the *detector* meter until it stops rising and type its indicated value in the same row under "*P* Intensity (mv)."

b) Proceed as in step vi above until all the target temperatures have been accounted for. Immediately rotate the *Volts* control CCW and switch off the power supply. *Save* the Excel spreadsheet. [Be especially careful as you approach the maximum target temperature. The lamp filament is designed to operate at rated electrical input at a maximum temperature of 2773 K. Beyond that temperature the tungsten filament begins to sublimate rapidly, and at 3700 K it melts.]

Analysis:

a) Directly under *Log T* enter =LOG(B2). Then *select* the cell and all the empty cells under *Log T* and *Log P* down to include the last row with data in it. (This can be accomplished by selecting the cell with "=LOG(B2)"in it, then holding down the shift key while moving the cursor to the last cell in the *Log P* column that should have data, that is, the one corresponding to the last row in use and then *left click.*) Then press *ctrl r* followed by *ctrl d*. All the selected cells should now be full with the appropriate data. *Save* the Excel spreadsheet.

b) You may print the Excel spreadsheet and use it to plot the graph, then draw a best-fit straight line and determine its slope. In that case when plotting the data suppress the origin and begin the *x*-axis at 1000 K. [If you are familiar with Excel and your lab instructor agrees you may use Excel to plot the graph, obtain the *Trendline*, and calculate the slope.] To just print the portion of the spreadsheet with your data, select all the filled cells and press *ctrl p*. In the printer window *left click* on *selection* and the number of copies that you want; then *left click* on *preview*. An image of the document appears. Select *setup* from the tool bar and select the *page* tab. Size the image to fit the page. Select the *sheet* tab and left click in the *gridlines* box. Close the *setup* window and select *print* from the tool bar.

c) If the data do not form a straight line with slope close to four, examine your procedures. Once you have identified the sources of errors correct them and repeat the entire procedure. This experimental setup and procedure is capable of better than 2% accuracy .

d) Determine the uncertainty of the calculated slope and attach it as error bounds to the slope value. Compare your slope to the well established theoretical and experimentally verified value of 4 by noting whether your slope and its error bounds include 4. Determine the percent deviation of the slope from 4.

Your Name   Course and Section   Date

Partner's Name   Instructor

30. Resistance, Ohm's Law, and i vs. V Curves

Objective: The dependence of the current through the component on the voltage across a component will be studied for a resistor, a light bulb, and a diode to gain an understanding of resistance, Ohm's law, unmeasured variables, and functionality of devices.

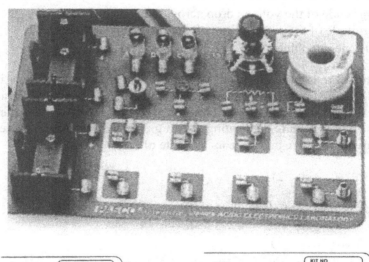

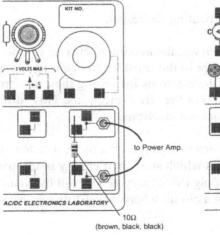

to Power Amp.

10Ω
(brown, black, black)

AC/DC ELECTRONICS LABORATORY

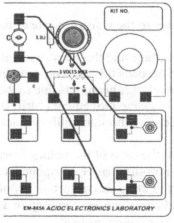

EM-8656 AC/DC ELECTRONICS LABORATORY

Description: A resistor, a light bulb from a flashlight (both "passive" devices), and a diode (an "active" device) are subjected to a voltage that varies between -V, +V, -V, +V in a smooth, ramplike, triangular manner as a function of time. The corresponding current through these devices varies with changing voltage. The current and voltage are studied graphically as a function of time for each device. Current vs. voltage is also graphed to convey the concepts of resistance, Ohm's law, unmeasured variables, and how a device functions.

Data studio provides a convenient power source that varies the voltage in this triangular manner while automatically graphing the voltage across the device and the current through the device. This power supply is "current limited" to 300mA. When the current reaches this value, the supply automatically limits the voltage, thus it no longer increases in the usual triangular fashion but becomes constant in value ("truncated") until once again the voltage value is such that the current is less than 300mA.

Theory: For a resistor operated in a current range where the device does not heat up appreciably, there is a linear relationship between the voltage and the current called Ohm's law.

$$V = iR \ldots\ldots\ldots\ldots\ldots\ldots 1)$$

where V = magnitude of the voltage drop across the resistor in volts (v)
   i = magnitude of the current through the resistor in amperes (A)
   R = resistance in ohm's (Ω)

The temperature therefore is an unmeasured variable that could affect the linearity of this relationship, namely equation 1) assumes a fixed temperature usually around room temperature of 70°F. To assure this is basically met, a resistor is given a power rating, e.g. 1W (watt), 10W, 100W etc. and grows dimensionally in size to distribute the heating over a greater volume as the power value grows. All the power to a resistor is dissipative and appears as a rate of heating.

$$P = Vi \ldots\ldots\ldots\ldots\ldots 2)$$

where P = power associated with an electrical component in watts (W)

$$P_R = i^2 R \ldots\ldots\ldots\ldots\ldots 3)$$

where P_R = power to the resistor = rate of heating the resistor

By knowing the wattage and the resistance values, the maximum current can be calculated. If one exceeds this current, damage to the resistor can occur (the resistor can "burn up"). On the microscopic level, this heating is due to the electrons increasing their random speeds due to the impressed voltage causing movement ("drift") of the "free" electrons. This "drift" speed translates into random motion increase through collisions among electrons.

One must note that the ratio of the voltage/current is not always the resistance. For example, capacitors and inductors are non-dissipative components which store their energy in electric and magnetic fields, respectively, and therefore can absorb or supply this energy in a circuit by changing their fields. Capacitors and inductors conserve energy in a circuit whereas resistors remove energy from a circuit and give it up to the environment as heat.

Initial Setup:
a) Connect the two outputs from the interface box to the two banana jacks on patchboard.
b) Open the "E & M" folder (electricity and magnetism experiments).
c) Open the "Ohm's Law1.ds" file.

Procedures: The interface box will act as a function generator and supply a repeating triangular voltage to each component under study in sections i) - iv). Section v) uses a constant voltage.

i) The resistor

a) Place a 10Ω resistor across the banana plug connections.
b) Click the **Start** button and observe how the voltage and current track with time. Note also how the current vs. voltage plot out in a repetitive straight line fashion.
c) Click the **Stop** button and print out the voltage and current vs. time graphs (both on the same plot) in landscape and label it "10Ω Resistor".
d) On the current vs. voltage graph, highlight the data and do a linear fit. The reciprocal of the slope (1/slope) is the resistance value.
e) Print out this i vs. V graph in landscape, label it "10Ω Resistor", and compare 1/slope to the value R = 10Ω.
f) Choose the maximum value of the current from this graph and calculate the maximum power to the resistor. Does it exceed the 0.5W rating of the resistor?

ii) Resistors in series and in parallel

a) Place two 100Ω resistors in series on the patchboard and wire to the banana jacks.
b) Click **Start** then after a short while click **Stop**.
c) Highlight the data set on the i vs. V graph and perform a linear fit to get the resistance (1/slope).
d) Print out this graph in landscape and label "Two 100Ω Resistors in Series"
e) Calculate the equivalent series resistance and compare to 1/slope value.
f) Now place the two 100Ω resistors in parallel and wire to the banana plug leads.
g) Click **Start** then after a short while click **Stop**.
h) Highlight the data set on the i vs. V graph and perform a linear fit to get the resistance (1/slope).
i) Print out this graph in landscape and label "Two 100Ω Resistors in Parallel"
j) Calculate the equivalent parallel resistance and compare to this slope value.

iii) The light bulb

a) Replace the resistor with a light bulb on the patchboard by running two wire between the bulb and the connections at the banana jacks.
b) Click the **Start** button and observe how the voltage and current track with time. Observe also the i vs. V graph.
c) You and your partner should coordinate so as to watch both these graphs and the light bulb itself. What happens to the bulb when the behavior begins to deviate markedly from linearity? What is happening to the resistance of the filament in the bulb?
d) Click the **Stop** button and print out the voltage and current vs. time graphs (both on the same plot) in landscape.
e) On the i vs.V graph, highlight the approximately "straight line" region near the origin, and perform a linear fit getting an approximate value for the filaments resistance in this region by taking 1/slope.

f) Print out all graphs in landscape and label them "Light Bulb".
g) Take the voltage/current ratio where current is maximum to get the maximum resistance value.
h) Calculate a maximum power for the light bulb. How does this compare to the 0.75W rating of the light bulb?

iv) The diode

a) On the patchboard replace the light bulb with the diode.
b) Click the **Start** button and observe how the voltage and current track with time. Observe also the voltage vs. current graph. What effect does the current limitation of 300mA from the interface box have on triangular voltage function.
c) Click the **Stop** button and print out the voltage and current vs. time graphs (both on the same plot) in landscape and label "Diode".
d) Calculate the ratio voltage/current from the "flat", current limited, region to get a resistance value for the diode in the "forward current" mode.
e) Calculate the power, Vi, in this "flat" region. How does this compare with the diode's 3W power dissipation rating?
f) Print out i vs. V graph in landscape and label it "Diode".

v) Varying the resistance

a) Exit the present experiment by clicking on **File** and then **Quit**, choosing **No** when prompted to save activity.
b) Connect the two outputs from the interface box to the two banana jacks on patchboard.
c) Open the "E & M" folder.
d) Open the "Ohm's Law2.ds" file.
e) A constant 5 volts is supplied across the two connections to the jacks and the current supplied to the jacks is displayed. Resistors of known value (10, 33,100,330,560,1000Ω)are connected successively across these terminals and V(5v), R, and i are recorded in a table.
f) Graph i vs. R in pencil. Circle the data points. Use drawing curve to run a smooth fit through the data set.

Questions:

1) Consider two circuits, both being connected to a constant 3-volt source. Circuit A has two light bulbs connected in series and circuit B has the same two light bulbs connected in parallel.

   a) Describe the relative brightness of the bulbs in one circuit in comparison to the other. Explain your answer using circuit analysis.

   b) Compare the power delivered to circuit A with that delivered to circuit B.

2) For ease of installation, a cabin that is used occasionally is supplied with baseboard electric heating. These are 30 amp circuits powered with 220 volts. To supply 70,000Btu/h (about 20kW),

   a) how many circuits are needed, and

   b) what is the resistance of each baseboard "strip" in a single circuit?

Your Name	Course and Section	Date

Partner's Name		Instructor

31. Mapping of the Magnetic Field from Helmholtz Coils

Objective: The magnetic field B, like force fields g and E, fills three-dimensional space. A pair of Helmholtz coils provides case of some importance for studying the spatial dependence of a field.

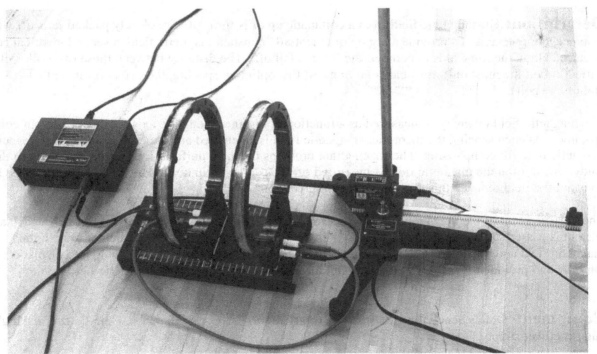

Fig.1. Setup for the axial scan of the magnetic field.

Fig.2. Setup for radial scan of the magnetic field in the midplane.

Description: The magnetic field from a coil made up of N turns of wire closely packed falls off with distance along its axis. To provide a region of essentially constant magnetic field, a second identical coil is placed along the same axis to compensate for this fall off. The distance between these two coils will be varied to find the most uniform field condition. At this optimum spacing, the two coils are called Helmholtz coils.

The magnetic field intensity is measured as a function of distance along the axis for three different coil spacings. At each spacing the theoretical magnetic field is calculated and superimposed on the measured magnetic field for comparison. The spacing that provides the most uniform field region is sought in this study. In addition the magnetic field is measured off axis at the optimum spacing setting again to see how constant the field remains this time in the radial direction.

The measurement of the magnetic field uses a Hall probe. This is a solid-state device through which a current is passed. In a magnetic field, moving charges experience a force perpendicular to both the magnetic field and the velocity. This causes the moving free charges of a particular sign to displace laterally and provide a small voltage which can be calibrated in terms of the magnetic field.

Equipment: Optics bench, linear translator, rotary motion sensor, Hall probe, Helmholtz coils, high current power supply

Theory:

Consider the magnetic field along the axis of a single current loop of radius R:

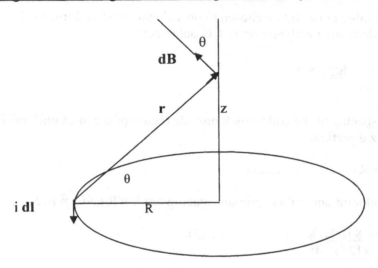

The law of Biot and Savart gives the relation between magnetic field and current:

$$d\mathbf{B} = \frac{\mu_0}{4\pi} \frac{i \, d\mathbf{l} \times \mathbf{r}}{r^3} \qquad \text{where } \mu_0 = 4\pi \times 10^{-7} \frac{\text{tesla·m}}{\text{A}}$$

Horizontal components will cancel in pairs, only the z-components are additive.

$$d\mathbf{B_z} = \frac{\mu_0}{4\pi} \frac{i \, dl \cos\theta \, \mathbf{k}}{(R^2 + z^2)}$$

$$= \frac{\mu_0}{4\pi} \frac{i \, dl \, R \, \mathbf{k}}{(R^2 + z^2)^{3/2}}$$

This integrates to

$$\mathbf{B_z} = \frac{\mu_0 \, i \, 2\pi R^2 \, \mathbf{k}}{4\pi(R^2 + z^2)^{3/2}} \quad\ldots\ldots\ldots\ldots\ldots\ldots\ 1)$$

For two such coils N turns each separated by distance h, with one coil centered at the origin (i.e. z = 0):

$$\mathbf{B_z} = \frac{\mu_0 \, Ni \, R^2 \, \mathbf{k}}{2(R^2 + z^2)^{3/2}} + \frac{\mu_0 \, Ni \, R^2 \, \mathbf{k}}{2[R^2 + (h - z)^2]^{3/2}} \quad\ldots\ldots\ldots\ldots\ldots 2)$$

To find what value of z will provide a maximum (or local minimum) in the magnetic field, set the derivative with respect to z equal to zero:

$$\frac{d\mathbf{B_z}}{dz} = 0$$

This gives as a solution the point on the z axis midway between the two coils,

$$z = h/2 \dots\dots\dots\dots 3)$$

At this midpoint field, the h value must still be chosen to provide the most uniform field. With B_z evaluated at $z = h/2$, set the derivative with respect to h equal to zero:

$$\frac{dB_z(z = h/2)}{dh} = 0$$

This gives as a solution the spacing of the coils which provide region of the most uniform field midway between the coils along the z direction:

$$h = R \dots\dots\dots\dots 4)$$

The magnetic field at the midpoint under this optimum spacing has $h = R$ and $z = R/2$:

$$B_z = \frac{8 \mu_0 N i k}{(125)^{1/2} R} \dots\dots\dots\dots 5)$$

The SI units on the B-field are teslas. To convert to gauss multiply by 10^4 (1 tesla = 10^4 gauss).

Moving charges in the Hall probe subjected to a magnetic field experience the Lorentz force:

$$F = q \, v \times B \dots\dots\dots\dots 6)$$

This force is perpendicular to both the velocity vector and the B-field vector and usually produces a spiral path for a constant speed particle.

Initial Setup:
  a) Study Fig.1 on the title page to become familiar with the experimental setup.
  b) Wires from the rotary motion sensor are plugged into digital channels 1 and 2 on interface box.
  c) The Hall probe wire plugs into analog channel A on the interface box.
  d) Coils are hooked up in series and then to the current supply.
  e) Open the "E&M" folder.
  f) Open the "HelmholtzCoil.ds" file.

Procedure and Analysis:

A) The axial magnetic field will be measured for three different spacings of the coils and compared to theoretical calculations.

  a) The Fig.1. setup will be used in this procedure. Make sure that the Hall probe will traverse along the axis beyond both coils.
  b) Measure the mean radius of the coils, R, and enter this value in data entry box below the graph.
  c) Set the mean spacing (distance between centers of coils), h =1.5R, and enter this value in the data entry box.
  d) Enter the number of turns in a single coil.

e) Before taking a data set, practice moving the Hall probe in a slow, smooth, and continuous fashion by rotating the pulley on the rotary motion sensor.

f) Check that the Hall probe switch is set to axial.

g) With the current off, click **START** and zero the Hall probe by pressing the Taar button. Then click **STOP** and pull down **EXPERIMENT** menu and **DELETE** the data run.

h) Set the current to 1A and enter this value in the data box.

i) Position the Hall probe outside the nearest coil (i.e. move to one extreme).

j) Click **START** and slowly rotate the pulley moving the Hall probe along the axis to the other extreme and click **STOP**.

k) Inspect the pattern. It should appear smooth and symmetric. If this is not the case, pull down **EXPERIMENT** menu and **DELETE** the present data. Then repeat the measurement procedure.

l) Using the **Smart Tool**, locate the position, z_{center}, which will lie in the middle of the valley (called a "saddle point"). Enter this value in the data entry box.

m) This will readjust the origin to place one coil at $z = 0$ and the other at $z = 1.5R$.

n) The theoretical curve should now be superimposed. Print out the graph in Landscape and label the graph with $h = 1.5R$.

o) Print out all the input parameters, i, R, h.

p) Next repeat the procedure with $h = 0.5 R$ and the current still at 1A.

q) Print out the graph and label with $h = 0.5 R$.

r) Print out all the input parameters.

s) Finally repeat procedure and printouts for $h = R$ and the current still at 1A.

B) With the spacing at $h = R$, the magnetic field intensity is measured in the radial direction in the plane midway between the two coils.

a) Turn off the current to the Helmholtz coils.

b) The Helmholtz coils at their optimum $h = R$ spacing are now repositioned so that the Hall probe will traverse the central plane parallel to the coils. Align the probe tip so its traverse takes it through the axis of the coils and covers the full diameter distance.

c) The switch on the Hall probe must be set to Radial.

d) With the current off, click **START** and zero the Hall probe by pressing the Taar button. Then click **STOP** and pull down **EXPERIMENT** menu and **DELETE** the data run.

e) Set the current to 1A.

f) Position the Hall probe at one extreme.

g) Click **START** and slowly rotate the pulley moving the Hall probe across the midplane to the other extreme and click **STOP**.

h) Inspect graph for smoothness and symmetry. With the **Smart Tool**, locate the center of the distribution, y_{center}. This should be the position of the axis.

i) Print out the graph in "landscape" and label "Midplane Traverse". Also write the y_{center} value on the graph.

Questions:

1) How uniform is the magnetic field around the midplane for $h = R$ setting? Give answer in terms of % deviation for ± 1cm, ± 2cm, ± 3cm, etc. first in the axial direction, then in the radial direction starting from the center point.

2) What energy would an electron have which orbits at a radius of 3cm in the magnetic field that was measured at the $h = R$ setting?

_____   _____   _____
    Your Name   Course and Section   Date

_____   _____
    Partner's Name   Instructor

32. Doppler Frequency Shift and Age of the Universe

Objective: When there is relative motion between the source of waves and the observer of those waves, the frequency of the detected waves are changed. This Doppler frequency shift will be measured for two cases of sound waves and the velocity of the source relative to the observer will be determined for these two cases. This Doppler shift will also be applied to light waves from distant stars whose velocity and distance from Earth can be determined. This will result in understanding Hubble's law, the Big Bang theory, and the age of the universe.

Fig.1. Doppler frequency shift for stationary detector and rotating speaker powered by function generator.

Equipment: Rotary Doppler Shift system with button speaker and microphone pickup, function generator, variable speed motor with control

Description:

The detected frequency is changed when there is relative motion between the source of the waves and the detector of those waves. This will be demonstrated with two cases of sound waves

1) Rotary Doppler Shift apparatus
2) Recording of a simulated Doppler shift

The challenge for a laboratory apparatus is to achieve sufficiently high velocities in a laboratory setting such that the frequency change is measurable. One solution to this problem is a rotary system. By providing a circular "tunnel" for the approaching and receding button speaker attached at the periphery of the rotating disk, the recorded sound from the stationary microphone should be identical to the frequency change in the linear motion case. This rotary system also has the advantage of providing a second precise method of determining source velocity based on the repeat sound pattern and the known circumference of the rotating disk.

Likewise electromagnetic waves demonstrate the Doppler shift effect but now the waves travel in empty space with the speed of light. This effect is applied in the monitoring of motorist speeds through frequency shifts in electromagnetic waves called radar and in understanding the severity of approaching weather patterns from the spread in frequencies using Doppler radar. But perhaps the most important insight that the Doppler effect has given the scientific community has to do with the red shift of the light from stars and galaxies in the universe. It is observed that this light is shifted to lower frequencies which means that these sources of light are receding from us. Furthermore, the further away the stars are from us, the greater their red shift and their velocity of recession. When plotting the velocities calculated from the red shift vs the distance to these stars, one obtains basically a straight line graph called Hubble's law. What is astounding in this is that to get such a result requires that all the matter in the universe started at a single point with an initial explosion called the "Big Bang". The inverse of the slope of the velocity vs distance graph results in the calculation of the age of the universe, i.e. the time elapsed since the "Big Bang" occurred. As a final exercise in today's experiment the frequency shifts (or rather the wavelength shifts) and distances of a set of galaxies will be given such that velocities can be calculated and Hubble's law demonstrated in a graph. A straight-line fit through the origin to this data set will allow a slope to be measured and the age of the universe calculated.

Theory:

Doppler shift of sound waves

The detected frequency f_O by a stationary observer in still air from an approaching source of sound emitting at frequency f_S can be expressed as

$f_O = f_S v / (v - v_S)$ ....1)   where v is the speed of sound in air and v_S is the speed of the sound source toward the observer.

The detected frequency f_O by a stationary observer in still air from a receding source of sound emitting at frequency f_S can be expressed as

$f_O = f_S \, v / (v + v_S)$ ....2)   where v is the speed of sound in air and v_S is the speed of the
                                                     sound source away from the observer.

The frequency difference between these two cases (assuming v_S is the same approaching and receding) is

$\Delta f = f_S \, v / (v - v_S) - f_S \, v / (v + v_S)$

$\Delta f = 2 f_S \, v \, v_S / (v^2 - v_S^2)$ ....3)

For case where $v_S << v$

$\Delta f = 2 f_S \, v_S / v$

$v_S = v \, \Delta f / (2 f_S)$ ....4)

In our two cases involving the Doppler shift of sound, this approximation will yield a result within 1% of the correct answer.

Doppler shift of light waves

Relativity provides the expression for the observed frequency f_O in terms of the source frequency f_S for the case where the observer and source are receding from one another at relative speed v:

$f_O = f_S \, (1- v/c)^{1/2} / (1+ v/c)^{1/2}$ ....5)

$\Delta f = f_S - f_O = f_S \, [1- (1- v/c)^{1/2} / (1+ v/c)^{1/2}]$ ....6)

$[1- \Delta f/f_S]^2 = (1- v/c) / (1+ v/c) = (1- v/c)^2 / (1- v^2/c^2) = (1- v/c)^2$ ....7)   for the case where v << c.

$v/c = \Delta f/f_S = \Delta\lambda/\lambda_S$ since $c = \lambda/T = \lambda \, f$ and thus $0 = \lambda \, df + f \, d\lambda$ therefore

$v = c \, \Delta\lambda/\lambda_S$ ....8)   where c is the speed of light, $\Delta\lambda$ is the magnitude of the shift in wavelength, and λ_S is the wavelength emitted by the source.

Temperature corrected speed of sound

The speed of sound increases with temperature because air molecules are in more rapid motion.

$v = (331 + 0.6 \, T_C)$ ....9)   where T_C is the lab room temperature in degrees Celsius.

Procedure and analysis:

Frequency change and velocity measurement with rotary system:

Caution! Do not try to stop rotating disk by hand. Let it slow down by itself.

a) Study Fig.1. The function generator is connected to the button speaker via the rotary contact. The microphone is connected to the analog input port A.

b) Open Doppler1.ds in the Sound folder.

c) The voltage output of the microphone will be plotted as a function of time giving the sinusoidal wave form associated with a pure pitch (i.e. a single frequency).

d) The frequency is set to 2300 Hz which is the resonant frequency of this solid state ("button") speaker. The amplitude is set on the function generator to about 1/3 maximum so as not to have a distorted signal.

e) The disk is rotated at a setting on the controller of fast, forward, adjust at 7. Once up to constant speed **Start** is clicked on. Then after about 10 rotations **Stop** is clicked. There should be about three repeat patterns per second.

f) Click on **Smart Tool** and position cross hairs on the peak of the final cycle. Print the full pattern out in landscape. Now position cross hairs on the peak of the first cycle and write the time associated above this peak.

g) Calculating the difference in the two times and dividing the number of cycle intervals by this time will give the repetition frequency. Multiplying this by the circumference will give the velocity of the source.

h) The approach frequency must be very carefully analyzed by counting large number of cycles since the effect is quite small. Spread the region just before the maximum in sound to cover a time interval slightly greater than 0.02 seconds. Then locate a peak with the **Smart Tool** near the right end of the display. Print out this graph in landscape. Now with cursor on the time axis, hand will appear. Move the time axis to shorter times still displaying the left end of the previous printed graph. Now using the **Smart Tool** locate a peak position on the left side of this new graph and print out. By counting the number of cycles (intervals) between these to time values and dividing by the time difference, the approaching frequency will have been determined. Show this detailed calculation on the graph and label the graphs Approach 1 and Approach 2.

i) Do the same to calculate the receding frequency. Print out graph and show the analysis on the graph and label graphs Recede 1 and Recede 2.

j) Calculate the velocity of the source using eqn.4 with speed of sound calculated from eqn.9. For f in the denominator use the average of the two measured frequencies. Compare source velocity to value determined in step g) (calculate a percent difference). Also convert this speed to miles per hour.

k) Now close Doppler1.ds.

Frequency change and velocity measurement from simulation:

l) Open Simulated Doppler2.wav in the Sound folder. Listen several times to this recording of a simulated Doppler shift. Close this application.

m) Open Doppler 2.ds in the Sound folder. This is a Data Studio recording of the sound you just heard.

n) Analyze the approach frequency and the receding frequency. Here the frequencies differ by a large amount.

o) Calculate the velocity of the source based on the change in frequency. Convert this speed to miles per hour.

Red shift in light from receding galaxies:

p) In the table below, calculate the receding velocity of the galaxies (See detailed instructions below the table).

q) Hand graph v vs D, fit best straight line to the data, and calculate the slope which is called the Hubble constant, H. Hubble's law is therefore written as v = H D.

r) The age of our universe is 1/H. The units of megaparsec/km/s are converted to years by multiplying by 10^{12}. Express the age of the universe in billions of years.

Location of Galaxy	$\Delta\lambda$ (Angstroms)	$v = c\, \Delta\lambda/\lambda$ (km/s)	D (megaparsecs)
Virgo	7.9		47
Ursa Major	181		169
Corona Borealis	292		340
Boates	497		720
Hydra	765		840

The K and L optical absorption lines of calcium have wavelengths of 3934 and 3968 angstroms (10^{-10}m) or an average wavelength $\lambda = 3951$ angstroms. The average shift of these wavelengths from that measured in the lab, $\Delta\lambda$, is listed in Table 1 for five galaxies. The velocity of these galaxies relative to earth can be calculated in the adjacent column where c = 300,000 km/s is the speed of light. The distance to the galaxy based on the apparent diameter of these similar galaxies is listed in astronomical units of megaparsecs. (A megaparsec is the distance light would travel in 3.3 million years!)

Question

1) Do a detailed conversion of megaparsec/km/s into years.

2) What would the Doppler frequency shift of a racing car be as it passes by the bleachers traveling at 210 miles/hour from the engine noise of 7000rpm (revolutions per minute)?

Notes

Notes

Notes

Notes

Notes

Notes

Notes

Notes

Notes

Notes

Notes